Academaze

Academaze

Finding Your Way through the American Research University

Sydney Phlox

AnnorlundaBooks

Cover illustration and design by Susan Lavoie. Cartoons by Sydney Phlox.

Editing services from Dora Dalton.

Published in the United States by Annorlunda Books.

Queries: info@annorlundaenterprises.com

First Edition

ISBN-13: 978-1-944354-09-1

In memory of my Nana, a true force of nature.

Contents

Foreword: What This Book Is About

The American academic landscape is vast, with a great diversity of institutions. There are schools that grant only two- or four-year degrees and those where one can undertake undergraduate, graduate, and professional studies. There are research universities and those focused primarily on teaching. Often, different campuses of the same university system have very different missions. There are public and private schools; the former were originally meant to provide high-quality, affordable education for in-state students, which they are pushed to continue to do despite the states' ever-decreasing support. Academia is dynamic and, for better or worse, reflects the changing priorities in the society.

I am a professor in a physical-science field at a large public research university in the United States. My university is one with very high research activity. These institutions are often referred to as major research universities (MRUs) or simply as R1s, based on the Carnegie Classification of Institutions of Higher Education. There are three aspects of any faculty member's job: research, teaching, and service. Their relative importance is tied to the institutional mission. At R1 universities, research that pushes the boundaries of human knowledge is the main focus. In the science, technology, engineering, and math (STEM) fields, a professor typically works with a group of graduate students and postdoctoral researchers ("postdocs" are PhDs who are getting additional training before transitioning to permanent jobs), along with technicians and research scientists in lab-based fields. The professor has to raise grants from federal funding agencies, industry, or private foundations in order to financially support his or her research program. This money pays the group-member salaries and benefits, tuition for the graduate students, equipment costs, reagents and other lab supplies, user fees for centrally maintained tools, and the so-called indirect costs (often referred to as "overhead") that the university takes in order to help support research. Teaching and service are important at research universities, but are decidedly secondary to developing and maintaining a vigorous and well-funded research program.

I think that an academic job at an R1 university is the best job in the world — I get to work with smart young people on intellectually challenging problems. But the job is demanding and the environment is competitive. It is not easy to get a tenure-track academic job at an R1, to secure tenure, or to maintain funding and research momentum. I don't think working at an R1 is harder than working elsewhere in academia; it is simply different, and in some ways considerably so. When you combine the different challenges and metrics of success at R1s with the fact that scientists and engineers on faculty at such institutions are a really small minority among the US professoriate, it is perhaps not surprising that I have always felt mainstream publications that discuss academia are not interested in or aimed at people like me. Of course, no one should shed a tear that the generally well-compensated scientists and engineers at large research schools — in many ways a privileged minority of all academics— don't get much space in the academic press. But this is part of the reason why most people have a wrong or incomplete picture of our professional reality. I think that's a loss, because I feel that what we do is interesting and important, and understanding it might help people better appreciate academia as a whole, as both an economic engine and the fountain of knowledge that it is.

With this collection of essays and cartoons, I hope to provide a window into the world of the sciences and engineering at a major research university, the world I know. The book arose from my nearly six years of blogging (2010–2015), initially at Academic Jungle and later at Xykademiqz. I don't recall exactly what prompted me to start blogging in the first place; I might have decided that I had some hard-earned wisdom to dispense after receiving tenure. Over the years, the blog became a virtual home, a place to connect with other academics, discuss the issues involving colleagues or students, and hone my writing skills. Yet, the world of academic science often feels like a very small place, especially for women in male-dominated fields. In order to speak honestly about my experiences, I blog pseudonymously and am publishing this collection under a pen name. I don't think my real-life identity matters, as long as I can paint a candid picture of the academic maze.

A significant portion of the book is devoted to the interactions with the people who make up academia: graduate students and postdocs, collaborators, colleagues, and administrators. Finally, as a woman in a STEM field, I face certain challenges — and, unfortunately, these are not confined to academia — that the men among my colleagues do not.

Considering that the book is focused on my experiences at a research university, it would be presumptuous to claim that it will be of interest to all academics, but I would be delighted if my colleagues in fields other than STEM or at schools with a different type of mission were to find something useful in it. I also hope that graduate students and postdocs, regardless of whether or not they intend to remain in academia, find it interesting to learn more about how their mentors live and work, and why they might be stressed out or demanding. Perhaps this book will somewhat humanize the mysterious creature at the other end of the advisor-advisee relationship, and help junior researchers find a way to build a more productive collaboration with their advisors.

As for any nonacademic readers who find their way to this book, I would love it if the book left them with a better understanding of what professors really do all day, and especially what they do all summer. (Sadly, it's not lounging poolside, eating bonbons.)

I am indebted to my great readers and commenters on both Academic Jungle and Xykademiqz, who were very supportive of the idea to distill my online writing into a book. I wish to thank Susan Lavoie, who designed the cover, and Dora Dalton, who copyedited the book. Special gratitude is due to Melanie R. Nelson of Annorlunda Books, whom I met through pseudonymous blogging, and who graciously offered to work with me on publishing this collection when all I had was a nebulous idea to use the blog material, somehow.

The greatest thanks go to my beautiful family, who gave me the space to undertake this project.

Sydney Phlox

Chapter 1

What Professors at Research Universities Actually Do

A Mysterious Vocation

A while ago, when I was picking up one of my children from a playdate and waiting for the kids to wrap up, I exchanged a few sentences with the little host's dad, whom I rarely see; he has an advanced degree, a professional one, and seems to work a lot. He asked if we had fun-filled plans for the summer, and I said that we would take a week off to go to a nearby vacationing spot and also have the kids at home around July 4th, but, other than that, my husband and I would work and the kids would go to camp or daycare. The dad was surprised and said, "But I thought you worked at the university!" And there it was again, the assumption that I am on vacation all summer because I don't teach.

I said that the local university was a big research university, where teaching was only a component of what faculty do, and that research was extremely important. I said that during the academic year professors were quite busy with teaching, especially when large undergraduate courses were involved, so summer was prime time to catch up on writing papers and proposals and to focus on advising graduate students. Then we talked a little about whether I worked in a lab and what I did, and it was cool to see his eyes light up at the mention of the word "quantum."

Around the same time, my husband and I finalized the refinancing of our house. While we were waiting for some paperwork to come back, we chatted with the mortgage lender, whom we knew fairly well as she had underwritten our original mortgage years ago. She had a lot of questions about what I do, what research entails, and how much I teach. I hope I managed to convey that running your own research group was a lot like running a small business, in the sense that you are responsible for funding and overseeing the people who work with you. She wanted to know what percentage of my time goes into teaching. That's a hard question to answer. I tried to convey that we have a nominal teaching load set by the college, and then research-active faculty get course-load reductions proportional to how much research activity they are engaged in. Also, it's very different to teach a 200-person freshman course versus a 20-student advanced elective or a graduate seminar.

I don't mind that people who've never been to college don't know what an academic job entails; to them, professors are just teachers. But when people who have been through college and even postgraduate education don't know what professors do, that's our own fault. Perhaps, in a way, this book is my attempt to help rectify that.

I do tell my undergrads what professors do and how research is funded. But I presume most people don't. Also, there are many students who go to schools that are not major research universities. I suppose it is true that many professors do take summers "off" in the sense that they cannot be found on campus. Some say, "No pay, no work" and perhaps travel for pleasure; some travel for work; some work from home. I can certainly be found on campus all summer, as long as I am not at a conference, as can most of my colleagues. Summer is an extremely busy time,

4

because students don't have classes and professors don't teach. There are also a number of proposal deadlines in the fall, so mad paper writing during the early summer gets replaced by mad proposal writing in the late summer and early fall.

I need to have a better response, which can convey to nonacademics, in a few short sentences, what we professors do. For instance, I could start by saying something like, "There are different universities, with some more focused on teaching and some more on research. Mine is one of the research-heavy ones, and the faculty are responsible for teaching undergraduate and graduate students, but a large portion of our time is devoted to doing research and supervising graduate students. Research is paid for by federal monies, for which we compete by writing grant proposals. Faculty are not generally paid by the university in the summer at all; our summer salary comes from grants ..." But then there are people who are 100 percent on soft money, how do I explain that to nonacademic folks? And there are all sorts of nuances in terms of institution type, field, seniority, group size ... And before you know it, people's eyes glaze over and you have lost them.

Things I Love about My Job

I have my dream job. I often think about how lucky I actually am to have this particular job — not just being a professor, but being one in this particular department. I am fortunate to be a part of a relatively harmonious collective — no, we don't all hold hands and sing "Kumbaya"; there are politics and there are disagreements, but the overall environment is generally healthy. Things get done and I think most people in the department really have similar professional values. When someone is successful, my colleagues first and foremost consider it a good thing for the whole department. I generally feel that I am a valued member of the faculty and that my opinion is respected. My intensity seems to be accepted and recognized as a force for good.

I am also usually really happy with my research group. Interactions with my smart and kind students are always an efficient way to lift my mood.

Random things I love about my job:

- Brainstorming and troubleshooting with my graduate students. Listening to two graduate students try to find their way out of being stuck. These are the best of times, because they show me how much the students have grown and how much they can do on their own. As a junior faculty member, I used to get frustrated when people got stuck; now I am just so excited for them, because of all the awesome things waiting on the other side of that dam that is just about to burst.

- Writing papers. It may be my absolute favorite part of the job altogether.

- Heck, all of writing. I even like writing grant proposals and responses to referees.

- My quiet, huge, early-morning undergraduate class, finally warming up and asking questions. Heads are nodding; there is even a spark in some eyes.

- Colleagues listening to what I have to say and appearing to respect me in a leadership role.

- My office. I have the best office in the world. It is large, bright, with high ceilings, and it is delightfully messy.

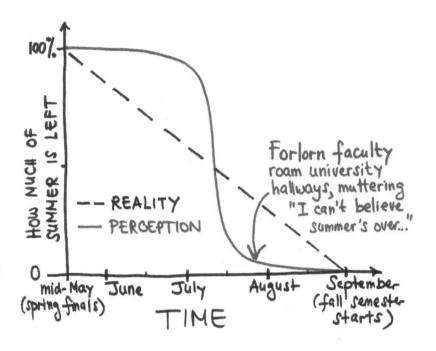

What Professors Do All Day When Not in Class

Have you ever wondered what we professors do all day when we don't teach? Well, wonder no more!

Here's what I did on an enforced "work at home" day, provided courtesy of a sick but recovering child:

- Reviewed two grant proposals for two different federal agencies (one US, one Canada).

- Reviewed one paper (revised version, didn't take very long).

- Wrote two letters of recommendation.

- Edited a full-length conference paper one of my graduate students was about to submit.

- Edited a colleague's paper, which I promised to do even though I also asked to be taken off the author list because I didn't do much for the project.

- Hastily submitted belated paperwork and a report for an existing grant, which I hope to get renewed, so I really should be behaving better toward the program manager.

- Filed paperwork for a no-cost extension of another grant.

- Organized and submitted paperwork for a recent trip.

- Filed justification for airfare for an upcoming trip.

- Booked yet another upcoming trip.

- Emailed fairly extensively with two of my grad students on technical stuff, and talked over the phone with one of them.

- Emailed lightly with three or four panicked undergrads, who realized the reign of terror is upon them as they are taking a class with me.

- Emailed with some 20 or so other people about various upcoming meetings or scheduling a classroom for the midterm exam in my huge class.

- Prepared a lecture for an upcoming class.

- Scanned some pages for student homework I had assigned, because the library for some reason didn't have the undergrad text on reserve yet.

- Organized and submitted paperwork to establish an undergrad's research position and add a grad student's MS to a PhD in another department.

- Read/skimmed two papers that a colleague sent me as of possible interest (they were).

- Worked on my annual report that was due in about a week.

- Worked on the figures for a manuscript that tentatively needed to be submitted within the next two weeks.

- Obsessed/fumed over the fact that a manuscript had been sitting on an editor's desk for several weeks without any action. OK, this is not work, but it takes energy. Even though it's mostly dark energy.

I didn't do the stuff I needed to do for a department committee I was on, or write the paper to accompany the invited talk I was giving the next month (I really shouldn't have accepted the invitation. I don't like to publish conference papers — too much time on something people don't read or cite). Two journal papers were nearing submission within the next month and a half, and a grant too; I was chipping away at those as well, but didn't get to them on that particular day.

Not bad for a "lazy academic" on sick-kid duty, huh?

Work Hiding in Plain View

I surprised the mother of one my kids' friends. She came to pick up her child from a visit and asked what I was doing, as I had my laptop out amidst mountains of paper associated with the proposals for large research centers that I was reviewing for a federal agency. I told her what my weekend had been and she was really shocked by me working over the weekend during the summer (not sure if it was the weekend, the summer, or both that was unexpected).

I, in turn, was surprised by the woman's reaction, as I had previously spoken with her a number of times about my job. This bothers me greatly, especially in the light of some recent conservative legislation. If a person who has access to information from the horse's mouth is incredulous about professors working weekends or summers (by the way, her husband works weekends all the time), what chance do we have of people who don't know any academics actually understanding what it is that we do? What if people see publicly available salaries at state schools, think that all we do is teach one course per semester, figure that's 4–5 hours per week tops, and we even have tenure! That certainly sounds outrageous. Most people employed by companies work long hours at lower salaries and with no job security. If I thought someone were getting away with good compensation, minimal work, and perfect job security, I might be livid, too.

If my kid's friend's mom doesn't know what professors do, what chance do we have with the general populace? How are we supposed to convince people that professors are not lazy, overpaid, and largely idle versions of K–12 teachers? (No disrespect to K–12 teachers intended: I know they work really hard.) How can we get it into the heads of the public that we are not the enemy, that yes, our jobs involve teaching their kids, but on top of that we conduct research, which in the sciences has many elements of running a small businesses: competing for funds, paying personnel, managing them, distributing the products (papers), but first giving between one-third and one-half of all the funds raised to the university in terms of overhead?

Americans are very hard-working people and have a great work ethic, which are some of the things that I really like about the society. But they distrust intellectuals, much more than I could say for any country in Europe or Asia that I have familiarity with. For instance, even in the rural areas in my home country, people would tell you that being a university professor is a distinguished vocation, alongside doctors and lawyers. Here in the US, doctors and lawyers are fine, as are corporate executives, but not professors. While I am sure few people actually know what it is that CEOs really do, they don't seem to begrudge CEO salaries. But those shifty university professors are certainly overpaid! People don't mind the truly outsize compensation and bonuses of individuals in certain careers, because those are somehow perceived as well deserved or earned, but as soon as the public thinks they're paying you through their state taxes, you are never considered to work enough to justify the investment. In reality less than 20 percent of a public university's budget comes from the state, and for many schools this percentage is in the single digits. A quick online search reveals 7 percent for the University of Michigan Ann Arbor, 5.8 percent at the University of Virginia, and 4.4 percent at the University of Colorado at Boulder.

One can argue that federal taxes also support universities, by providing funding for academic research. Receiving federal funds to do research is a very competitive process, with funding rates of roughly 10 percent across funding agencies. Grant proposals are complicated documents that are heavily scrutinized by one's scientific peers and the funding-agency administration before a project is recommended for funding. As someone who has served on panel reviews many times, I can assure you that there are many more well-thought-out, meritorious projects, any of which would result in new knowledge or applications, than there is money to fund them. More, rather than less, spending on science is what an economically prosperous and forward-looking country needs. I don't know what we can do to convince the public that we do an important job, that many of us would make considerably more in industry and that tenure is a way to attract talent, and that research at the US universities is an important economic engine. It is not popular to speak of broadening students' horizons or instilling critical thinking skills in the face of rising tuition costs and college debt. But we also can't let people believe whatever they want, because this public opinion is a base for squashing research funding and state support for public universities. We can't stop trying to get through to the people around us about what we do and why it's important — for them.

Chapter 2

The Academic Job Search

An Insider's View of a Faculty Search

Every faculty search starts at the level of an academic department. There may be a more-or-less formal mechanism by which the department decides when new hires are needed, depending on the department culture and size. In midsize (20–40 faculty) and large (over 40) departments, it's sometimes a tug of war to decide which area gets priority for new-faculty recruitment. It helps if the department administration has a strategic plan for hiring, and keeps a record of who hired last and how successful the recent searches in different areas were. Some areas might have the potential to bring in more money than others; it should not matter, but it does. Some departments prefer to be the best place to do A and B, rather than just another place to do A through F reasonably well. As a result, such places will hire more in the areas where they are already strong. Other departments might want to expand into new fields, in which case they will hire several people in rapid succession, at least one of whom will be a prominent senior figure.

Assuming the department can get its act together and decide on what it needs, a case has to be made with the higher administration, which generally starts with the college dean. The department may or may not get to hire, depending largely on the college budget, but also on the college strategic plan (yes, there are such documents and people do rely on them), how recently the department last hired, if they had retirements or faculty leaving for other institutions, and the general standing of the department in the college pecking order or among the dean's favorites.

If things go well, the department will get a green light to hire no later than early fall, and will be able to advertise in the October–December timeframe and generally interview as early as January, but typically February through April.

Being on the search committee is a lot of work. Committee members really look hard for the best candidate, but also one who is likely to accept. Candidates with top pedigrees who don't botch interviews tend to want to stay within their crème-de-la-crème academic echelon. Every year there are one or two such hot commodities on the job market, whom everyone interviews and everyone gives an offer to, which I think is silly — having 20 offers is good for such a candidate's ego, but most schools should really consider whether these people are realistic hiring prospects. I know, that would mean the department admitting that they don't consider themselves to be tippy-top, which brings out interesting aspects of the collective self-consciousness. Do we pretend we are more awesome than we are and go for the fanciest candidate, but then get turned down? If we are lucky enough to have two candidates the department likes, they are both generally outstanding and either one would make a great colleague and a successful faculty member, should we make the offer to the one we judge to be more likely to accept?

Faculty searches are quite draining for existing professors. A lot of emotional energy goes into it; we all want to hire someone good, we get excited about promising candidates, we get irritated by those who have failed to prepare or who look downright disinterested and thus waste our time. Candidates (understandably) don't realize how many meetings each of us on faculty has in regards to each search, even without the time spent talking to the candidates. When you are on the search committee, you also have a higher-than-average obligation to take interviewees to lunch or dinner, meet with each individually, attend every talk, and partake in discussions after each visit.

After the interviews are over, there is a potential lack of consensus as to who the best candidate is. In my experience, in very strong, high-performing areas, people tend to agree pretty quickly on whom they want. In others, you have more strong-personality interference, territoriality (sometimes senior but inactive people block the hiring of someone junior who is perceived as a threat), and other considerations that may result in the most promising candidate not getting the offer.

I am in a large enough department that I have seen all sorts of scenarios play out. We are lucky to have a smart chair who has the best interests of the department at heart, as well as considerable political savvy to pull it off and forward our agenda, without irritating the college administration.

Based on what I have seen, here is my advice to faculty candidates: Apply wherever you appear to be a reasonably good fit, with "reasonably good" and "fit" interpreted very liberally. If the call is vague, that often means the department is open to seeing who's out there before deciding on an area to prioritize. If you get an interview, congratulations! But even if you think you did great, you as a candidate have no idea about what is going on in terms of internal politics, so it's best not to obsess about it, as there is nothing you can do. There may be some who liked you when you interviewed, but if the department priorities or loudest mouths are elsewhere, you are toast. I know this is hardly a consolation, but it is what it is. All you can do is try to do your best. You'll get better at interviewing with more practice, and you'll get better at realizing what it is that you want in a potential home department.

Surviving the First Cut

Being on a faculty search committee is a lot of work, but as far as faculty service obligations go, this one is really worth it, because you have an influence over who your future colleagues will be and where the department will go in the long run.

The committee work involves sifting through hundreds of applications in order to choose 3–5 who will be invited for an on-site interview. We don't do phone or Skype interviews, but some departments do. Our committees consist mostly of people with the expertise in the targeted area within the department, but also one or two people outside of it. Everyone on our committee sees every application, but I am sure there are committee-to-committee variations, e.g., some may split the application piles, so each file is seen by only one person. The process of selecting interviewees usually involves several steps. The first cut is the most drastic one, which the vast majority of applications don't survive, as the several-hundred-application pile is reduced to a few tens — the long list. Each committee member makes their own first cut and then we compare and compile; it's always amazing to me how much overlap there is among different people's long lists. Input from others in the department may be solicited at this stage. Then the committee meets once or twice to discuss the people on the joint long lists and reduce the number to a short list of 3–5, with perhaps a couple of alternates. These 3–5 need to get approved by the department executive committee (all tenured faculty) and the college dean before they can be invited to an interview. Therefore, the candidates must have some pretty apparent markers of future excellence that are defensible in front of the colleagues and the dean.

You, the applicant, need to survive the first cut and make the long list of at least one but preferably several people on the search committee. If you make no one's long list, it is highly unlikely that anybody will give your application a second look. This process is not unlike panel review of proposals — someone has to notice you and want to champion you.

When I have hundreds of applications to sift through and the search is defined pretty broadly, there are three things that I immediately look for: your area of expertise, where you did your PhD and postdoc, and your publication record. Which first brings us to …

Documents: Different searches request different paperwork, but every search will ask for a cover letter and a curriculum vitae (CV). Some will want your research and teaching statements. Some will ask that the references send letters right away, some just want the names of the references and will solicit letters if you are nearing inclusion on the short list. Always, *always*, submit a cover letter, a CV, as well as the research and teaching statements. Yes, even if the ad does not explicitly ask for the last two, submit them anyway. Why? Because others do, and even though your application must technically be considered if you submitted the minimal required paperwork, once you are nearing inclusion on the short list, it helps if people know more about what you plan to do and how.

However, in order to survive the first cut, your past record is key, so your CV is the most important document. During the first round of screening, I only look at the CV, along with a few quick glances at the cover letter. The following information gets retrieved during the initial screening.

Area of expertise: In both the cover letter and the CV, state prominently what your subfield is, or what your two to three broadly defined areas of interest are. I am grateful if within five seconds of opening your application I know what it is that you are an expert in. Here's the rub — sometimes the faculty search ad is vague on purpose in terms of area, because the department wants to cast a broad net and just hire whoever looks best. Sometimes it is vague because the department did not decide ahead of time what the priorities were. Sometimes there are well-defined priorities, but they are not in the ad for all sorts of reasons. All you, as the applicant, can and should do is apply if the search appears to be even remotely receptive to your expertise and then keep your fingers crossed. There is no point in trying to guess what is behind the ad. Ads are crafted as much (or more) by HR as by the department, and the wording often leaves much to be desired. Faculty-job ad craftsmanship often brings to mind the proverb "Too many cooks spoil the broth."

Pedigree and publications: Your pedigree — where and with whom you got your PhD and did your postdoc — is very important. We all believe that people who went to top schools must be very smart to get in, that they get a quality education once in, and have reputable people vouching for them, so it's hard to deny that pedigree matters. However, it is not enough. How your publication list looks is *very* important. If you have a PhD and a postdoc with many first-author papers in reputable journals, you are the person I want to see.

If you are serious about an academic position in a science field, you feel you have what it takes to do the job, but you are getting a PhD at a good but not great school, you have to publish as much as possible, more than a person from a more prestigious institution. If your field requires a postdoc, you should try to get into a good, productive, and, if possible, prominent group at a better university, where "better" generally means "better name recognition." And keep publishing like your life depends on it. I know, this is easier said than done, as postdoc advisors are not the world's most nurturing demographic, especially those who are very successful at cutthroat places. A bad match with a postdoc group can derail your career for good, which is why you need to be as careful and as informed as possible when trying to find the optimum combination of productivity and pedigree boost. As in all things career-related, it also doesn't hurt to be a little lucky.

It may seem like the first cut during a faculty search is made somewhat crudely. However, among hundreds of applications, the truth is that the vast majority are simply not competitive at all — these applicants will never get a faculty position. I am probably wrong about a handful of them, but not about most. In an ideal world, someone would tell these people that their applications don't look competitive for the type of position they seek. But then again, all sorts of unconscious biases can creep up into this type of advice, so perhaps it's better to just let people apply. But you, the applicant, can certainly try to talk to your PhD and postdoc advisors and find out what a typical record of a recent tenure-track hire looks like. You can also go online and look at the websites of assistant professors at the institutions where you envision working, count their publications, and see how you measure up.

Know Thy Friends

Professors are frequently asked to write letters of reference: recommendation letters for undergrads applying to grad school, for graduate students and postdocs seeking postdocs or jobs; evaluation letters for tenure-track faculty who are being considered for tenure, as well as for faculty at various career stages who are being nominated for honors and awards. If I agree to write a letter for someone, I will not write a negative one. If I cannot, in good conscience, write one that is positive, then I will refuse to write a letter entirely.

If someone gets a PhD degree in my group, I endorse that person and vouch for them. The PhD is thicker than water! It's not without reason that a PhD advisor–advisee relationship constitutes a lifetime conflict of interest in the context of the NSF proposal review. I will write letters for students and postdocs as often and for as long as they need them, until one of us drops dead. I would never have a problem with any of my former students or postdocs seeing the letters that I have written for them.

In regards to tenure-track applications, letters of reference become important once a candidate has survived the first and often even the second cut. The PhD and postdoc advisors are at the top of the reference list for most faculty applicants, which indicates that the candidate considers them someone on whose enthusiastic support he or she counts. In the vast majority of cases, this trust is warranted: the PhD and postdoc advisors promptly respond to the requests for letters and send recommendations that are detailed, informative, and usually glowing. This expediency holds even for the busiest and most famous among former advisors, which goes to show that if something is important to a person, they will find the time to do it.

Then there are others …

I know a successful mid-career colleague who did not put his PhD advisor on the list of references at all back when he was first applying for tenure-track jobs. I don't even think the two of them got along that poorly; the colleague published a lot and well as a grad student, but I can imagine he might have been a handful because he has a very strong personality. I really don't think the advisor would have written a bad letter, but I suppose you never know. The colleague had decided he had stronger and more enthusiastic references elsewhere and, while he knew this conspicuous absence of the PhD advisor's letter raised red flags with some hiring committees, he was ultimately able to land a good tenure-track position and is now very successful.

Here is my favorite from a few years back: the PhD advisor wrote a paragraph-long email, basically saying the candidate was good and productive. Nothing bad, but it's still just a paragraph. It raised all sorts of questions among the faculty search committee and I believe contributed to this candidate not getting an offer from us.

I have seen cases where the PhD advisor or the postdoc advisor is near the bottom of a lengthy list of references. Usually, from the CV, you can see a clear correlation between this ordering and the candidate not having published very well during the PhD/postdoc. In a few cases, the advisor had a reputation as being very difficult to work with. Unfortunately, all this does cast a shadow of doubt on the applicant, but it does also reveal that the applicant knew that the advisor was not to be counted on. Having a so-so relationship with the PhD advisor can be remedied by a great postdoc. Unfortunately, candidates with a great PhD but a ho-hum postdoc, or a good first but not a great second postdoc, don't usually fare well on the academic-job market. In academia, a junior researcher is only as good as his or her last few papers.

I also remember the case of an applicant from a few years ago, who looked great on paper, had a great record from his PhD, and listed his PhD advisor as first reference. The reference letter from the advisor never came, even after reminders. Before you wonder whether the advisor had died, become incapacitated or otherwise indisposed, I should tell you that the advisor did submit letters for other candidates in the same search. So the absence of a letter was definitely meant to convey a lack of endorsement. Whether or not this was a petty or a real issue, it hurt the candidate. What is most surprising to me is that the candidate was not aware that there was an issue, that the advisor would not be supportive. Maybe the advisor was sneaky and passive-aggressive, or even openly deceptive — all sweet on the outside, but seething with rage and disappointment on the inside. Could it simply be delusion on the part of the candidate, refusing to believe that the advisor would not provide support? Could it be that everyone's egos were just a little too big for the candidate's good?

Some professors are not nice people. Some students are not nice people, either. Sometimes there is just too much of a mismatch between what the two parties expect from one another. In an ideal world, the advising relationship would be dissolved in these cases and the junior person would go work for someone more supportive. In an ideal world, people would also talk openly, and the advisor, who holds considerable power over the student/postdoc, would be able to convey what they are unhappy about and what needs to change. But, this is not an ideal world, so you, the candidate, had better rely on your gut and common sense and try to be honest with yourself as to how much support you can realistically expect and from whom during the application process, because the competition is so fierce that committees will readily relegate you to the "do not interview" list if there are doubts cast upon your merit by the people who are supposed to know you best.

Still, do not despair at these unfortunate anecdotes — most PhD and postdoc advisors are fiercely supportive of their group alumni. Chances are, your advisor is in this group.

Notes from the Search

The process of faculty hiring often reveals more about the colleagues with whom I interact in regards to the search than it does about the candidates.

My school is a large and reputable public school and the department is highly ranked. We are nothing to sneeze at, so I think it makes sense to look for a candidate who actually wants to come here, as opposed to someone who is settling for us. No one knows what tomorrow brings, but I want a candidate who, at the time of signing the contract with us, is genuinely excited about joining the department and enthusiastic about all the years of hard work and collaborations ahead.

I don't want a candidate who is taking this offer because we were the safety school and they didn't get any offers from any of the several schools where they also interviewed, all located in a specific, widely desirable part of the country far from here, where he or she would greatly prefer to go. This candidate will likely be out of here before you can say "failed faculty search," because they never actually wanted to be here, anyway.

One straw-man counterargument that has occasionally been raised is why you would want someone who can't leave. Shouldn't you want someone who is very good and can leave whenever they want?

I don't want someone who can't leave. I want someone who can leave but *doesn't want to*, at least not before the ink dries on the contract. Signing that tenure-track offer letter is like getting married — you better be enthusiastic about it on your wedding day, otherwise what's the point? Sure, people "get divorced" from their institutions and move on, but if you don't actually want the commitment from the get-go, better not do it at all. Starting up a lab costs money, searches require energy and time. I know that the loss of each faculty member due to moving or retirement disrupts the department. I don't like the attitude that we should be grateful to get the "best possible person" if even for a few years. That argument is based on a fallacy that there is such a thing as the one best person. In fact, there are many excellent people who would do great if given the chance. I don't want someone who will be entirely focused on getting out of here from day one, for I cannot imagine such a person would be a very good colleague, collaborator, or contributor to the department.

Feelers

I have been a professor for over a decade. I am good at what I do and respected within my community. I am well funded, although that's always a temporarily accurate statement, and have always been able to support a viable research group. I publish in well-respected society journals, interspersed with some high-profile papers. My students are great and have been able to get good jobs after graduation. We look at interesting problems and publish papers that I would like to think are original, insightful, and well written. I am successful, even if I don't think I am wildly so.

Over the past few years, I have been getting "feelers" from other institutions with increasing frequency. Usually it goes along the lines of me going to give a talk, and then several people asking me if I am happy where I am and what my husband does and if I would consider moving/leaving my university. I used to think people were just making conservation; I was very naive. Nobody asks you about your happiness and well-being unless they are your mother, a close personal friend, or they have a very good and far-from-selfless reason to ask.

So far, the feelers have come from places that would represent a lateral or even a slightly downward professional move, but potentially with a lot of money. A few came from places that are in growth mode. In contrast, my current place is very good, but with some unsettling markers of stagnation. Declining state support has everyone tightening their belts, wondering what comes next; the college has lost a number of successful mid-career faculty.

The biggest reason I am not considering moving at this time is my family. If it were up to me alone, I would move. I hate the weather and might move for the sunshine alone. Another reason is that, as much as I have been willing myself to love the city I live in, I just don't. We don't really have good friends here. There are some couples we see on occasion, but I doubt any of them would be shattered if we left. We are situational friends — friends only because life threw us together, not because we are particularly compatible or drawn to one another — and, after all the years here, it's likely that situational friends are all we will have. We are too foreign, too accented, and too godless for the locals, so we are not even bothering any more with anyone we don't know from work.

But with the crappy cold weather come good public schools. My children have real childhood friends and memories tied to this place. A colleague from a fairly traditional culture says that his kids get no say in what he does professionally; if he gets a good offer and decides to move, they move, end of story; he says he doesn't care what the kids think or feel about the ordeal. I just couldn't bring myself to move my happy, well-adjusted teenager across the country midway through high school.

I would love for the place where I am now to become a place I am content with both professionally and personally. It's a very good place professionally, but it could be better for me, specifically. For instance, during a visit to my alma mater some years back, I was reminded how nice it was to have several faculty in the same area, who could collaborate and go for bigger grants and even take care of each other's students. I remember loving the fact that I was part of a large, probably 30-student group of all these different professors together when I was in graduate school. In contrast, my students are somewhat isolated, in that there is no one else at my current place of employment who does work similar to mine. While I can have my pick of collaborators, being the only one is quite limiting— I don't have the bandwidth to do all the things I could potentially do. It's also quite taxing on me that I am the only source of technical knowledge in my subarea. Where I went to school, there was a wider variety of courses offered between the three or four professors in the subarea; here, it's just me. This is a problem because my graduate students can't take the courses they need unless I teach them, yet these days I rarely do as I am often busy teaching undergrads.

On the other hand, both undergraduate and graduate students are pretty good at my school. Or, I should perhaps rephrase: one can handpick very good students, who come for the school's reputation, have a strong background in math and physics, and are highly motivated.

If I didn't have a family, I would move someplace warmer, where there are other people doing what I do and where I would be paid a lot. Actually, if it were just me, I would probably move every four to five years, as I tend to get bored. But I have a husband who is very happy with his job and kids who are very happy with their schools and friends.

This whole feeler business and the possibilities of going someplace can make me restless; they are enticing, and possibly even more so since I can't really act on any of them. I don't want to make the people interview me formally and give me offers when I know I am tied down. (Many people do precisely this, make the other institution interview and make a formal offer just to get leverage with their home institution. I won't, because I think it is a waste of everyone's time to string people along unless you are seriously considering moving.) I am not unhappy or unproductive where I am; the feelers don't come from the places that would be a blatantly obvious step up. (Do you hear that, MIT and Stanford? I am still waiting.) There is no pressing reason to move, except my restlessness, dislike of cold, and lack of good friends. There are reasons to *not* move, such as uprooting my family from a good situation, which includes good public schools and a solved two-body problem, for essentially no reason.

Ah, possibilities. And at the same time, impossibilities.

Upgrading Institutions Mid-career

A reader question: What are the chances for a productive faculty member from a low-ranked university to move to a quality R1 (an institution with very high research activity) mid-career? Does anyone really sympathize that the effort to get things done at a low-ranking school might turn into much better results at a quality R1? Is it really much harder to move with tenure?

Based on my observation of the people who have either moved away from my institution to another or whom we have recruited after they had become established elsewhere, it is certainly possible to move laterally or somewhat upward without being a superstar. The question is always what you bring to the new institution. If you are a respected name and have a niche, you will find a place that wants you, but it may take some time and you probably need to send out some feelers through trusted colleagues. It is about the fit — your expertise may be redundant at one place, but sorely lacking at another.

Moving mid-career generally requires that you have an "in," someone who will champion your case. This is considerably more common than getting an interview after applying cold. One reason is that you would have to be brought in with tenure, so colleagues have to commit to spending decades by your side without the acclimating probationary period of the tenure track. That is why it is very important to have someone with a strong interest in bringing you in. For example, there is a person who is being strongly advocated for these days in my department. That person is very good, but I would not say a superstar, yet they have already moved several times in their career (at least four or five), with most of the moves lateral-ish. This person has a whole collective of long-time collaborators in several departments at my university, and these people are jointly putting a lot of pressure on the department and college to make things happen.

If you have been very active at a lower-tier institution, people will be impressed, but I don't think you can count on them imagining all the wonderful things that you could have done if only you had had more resources. Instead, I would go for the following mindset: forget that you are at a lower-tier institution. Tell yourself that you are as good as anyone else; these are your specific technical strengths and this is what you are known and respected for; you deserve to be at a strong R1. Now, what is it that you bring to certain institutions that they already don't have? Many R1 departments pick several areas that they want to be leaders in, and then hire to develop those areas to be as strong as possible; in this scenario, you would be filling a specific need within an existing strength. Other times, a department may have just decided (after some strategic planning) to start developing a new area, one they previously didn't have. Such development usually starts by bringing in someone who's mid- or even late career, ideally with great name recognition. However, not all places are able to afford a superstar. If you are at a lower-ranked R2, maybe first jump to a top-ranked R2/lower-ranked R1. There are many very good schools in this group. You could be that productive senior person who helps them start a program in an area they haven't had before. Then, a few years later, upgrade further to a better R1, if that is still what you want to do. If you are at a lower-ranked R1, perhaps go for a mid-range R1 first, then even higher after a few years.

Ultimately it is about what you bring to the institution, and having colleagues there who are willing and able to go to bat for you.

Chapter 3

The Tenure Track

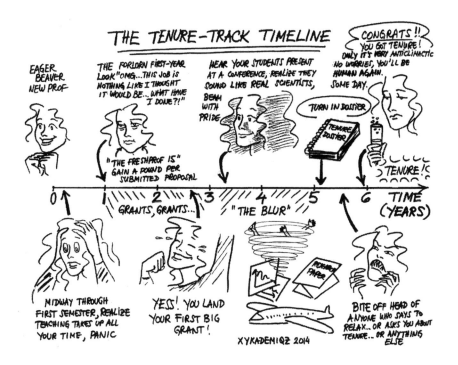

THE TENURE-TRACK TIMELINE

CONGRATS!! YOU GOT TENURE! ONLY IT'S VERY ANTICLIMACTIC. NO WORRIES, YOU'LL BE HUMAN AGAIN... SOME DAY.

EAGER BEAVER NEW PROF

THE FORLORN FIRST-YEAR LOOK "OMG...THIS JOB IS NOTHING LIKE I THOUGHT IT WOULD BE... WHAT HAVE I DONE?!"

HEAR YOUR STUDENTS PRESENT AT A CONFERENCE, REALIZE THEY SOUND LIKE REAL SCIENTISTS, BEAM WITH PRIDE

TURN IN DOSSIER

TENURE!

"THE FRESHPROF 15" GAIN A POUND PER SUBMITTED PROPOSAL

TENURE DOSSIER

0   1 2 3 4 5 6   TIME (YEARS)

GRANTS, GRANTS...   "THE BLUR"

MIDWAY THROUGH FIRST SEMESTER, REALIZE TEACHING TAKES UP ALL YOUR TIME, PANIC

YESS! YOU LAND YOUR FIRST BIG GRANT!

RESEARCH PAPER

XYKADEMIQZ 2014

BITE OFF HEAD OF ANYONE WHO SAYS TO RELAX.. OR ASKS YOU ABOUT TENURE... OR ANYTHING ELSE

The First Few Years As an Assistant Professor

How does one successfully manage the first few years on the tenure track? My advice is for a physical-science field at a major research university in the US, but some of it is broadly applicable.

1) Teaching. Try to make sure you teach graduate courses in your specialty rather than large-enrollment undergrad ones in the first two or three years. Teaching well takes a lot of time, particularly when you are first starting out. Teach the same couple of courses a few times during your first few years, until you get your research program going. Ideally, senior faculty mentors will be there to advise you and be your advocates, shielding you from unnecessary burdens. Many universities have formal mentoring programs; take advantage of them.

2) Start-up. You probably received a start-up package that covers equipment, stipend and tuition for a couple of research assistants (RAs) for two to three years, and some travel and summer salary money.

2a) Summer salary. In the US, it is common for physical-science faculty to have nine-month contracts. The summer salary at research universities is usually covered by research grants, and a tenure-track faculty member is expected to eventually bring in enough extramural funds to pay their own summer salary. However, it is typical for a start-up to include funds to cover a couple of months of summer salary for a couple of years, until you land your first grant (or five).

2b) Personnel. Try to recruit one or two grad students who will start during your first year, or bring in a postdoc whose quality you trust to help you build up your lab. You need people right away, but you don't have to immediately bring in everyone you think you will ever need. There is a learning curve when it comes to recruiting people, so your first few hires may be awesome, but they may be duds, too. Keep your fingers crossed.

2c) Equipment and building a lab. These things take considerable money and time. Start shopping right away. However long you think it will take, it will be much longer.

3) Funding. In the physical and biological sciences, it is expected that you will raise extramural grants from federal agencies. Getting funding is probably your highest priority at the start. For certain agencies, it is important to make personal connections with program managers, so you will have to travel to Washington, DC, to meet them and see where their interests lie. Map out all the early-career/young-investigator awards for which you are eligible (some have limitations on how many years post-PhD you can be when you apply), see how many tries you have for each one, and what you need for each. Hit as many of them as you can, potentially staggering them, but generally hit them hard. A few are due in the summer, so you have a full year of practicing with regular National Science Foundation (NSF) proposals and collaborative proposals before the first wave of those young-investigator awards.

A bit of parenthetical info: People in the physical sciences tend to be part of a university's College of Letters and Sciences (L&S) or College of Engineering (computer science and materials science, for instance, could be in either, depending on whether they are standalone or associated with an engineering department). The funding requirements in a College of Engineering are generally different as a whole than in L&S. There are fewer teaching assistantships available in engineering because the departments do not teach service courses and everyone is expected to bring in multiple grants. Among the departments in L&S, there are also differences. For instance, chemistry and biochemistry will typically have high requirements on grants, similar to chemical engineering, but often have larger groups because of the supply of teaching assistants. People in statistics, computer science, and some branches of engineering and applied math have very similar requirements as to how much money should be raised and the publication pace. In the physics departments, condensed-matter experimentalists will raise money and publish at a pace similar to chemists or materials scientists, while theorists in general and people in particle physics or astrophysics may not be facing high grant-raising requirements, and grants may not be an important part of tenure review in those fields. In some math departments, it is specified at tenure time that they do not consider grants as a measure of excellence.

In general, in Colleges of Engineering, grants will be a significant component of the tenure evaluation. If you are in L&S, depending on the field, grants may or may not be considered as a metric of accomplishment. Learn early what matters in your department.

4) Papers. If you have data from a previous postdoc or some collaboration, write those results up for publication during the first year. Alternatively, write a review paper or two. Backlogged, collaborative, or review papers are a good way to bridge the gap between starting a new lab and having papers come out of it (which realistically won't happen right away). Depending on what you do, you could also have single-author papers; I did during the first few years on the tenure track, while my first students were being trained.

5) Service. Keep institutional service minimal and maximize the professional service that will enhance your visibility and potential for getting funds. Travel to see program managers, travel to give invited talks and lectures. Do not organize a major conference as a new assistant professor, but do participate on program committees if invited. Definitely volunteer to review proposals for relevant agencies, both on panels and ad hoc; these experiences will drastically help improve your grant-writing abilities.

6) It gets better. The first few years on the tenure track are crazy, but you will get into the swing of things by the end of year three. Try to be nice to your colleagues, but avoid unnecessary obligations in terms of teaching and service. Your primary duty is to get your research program up and running — which means grants and papers — and anyone who is trying to divert your time is not your friend early on the tenure track. Once you have gotten your first couple of grants, have papers coming out, and have several students staggered in seniority, it's OK to diversify your teaching (e.g., show you can teach undergrads, try novel classroom techniques) and service (ideally something you care about, like curriculum or facilities or new faculty recruitment).

Support on the Tenure Track

(Originally appeared in Inside Higher Ed)

In an ideal world, you would start your new academic job as a tenure-track faculty member in a harmonious department, where professors are all good friends, where everyone is well funded and adequately supported with facilities and resources, and all students are both brilliant and highly motivated. In reality, people often don't get along, there are nowhere near enough resources or staff support, and working with students is much more demanding than you envisioned. In this real world, adequate support from your department's faculty and staff, as well as the university, is critical for the development of your research program and your success in getting tenure, and — last but not least — your personal satisfaction and peace of mind.

How do you get adequate support while on the tenure track? I write here for a tenure-track faculty member in a first appointment at a research university, but most of the issues discussed here can likely be generalized to other types of institutions as well as to non-tenure-track faculty.

Adequate facilities and resources. In the sciences and engineering, the quality of individual lab space and shared facilities can make or break one's career. Unfortunately, many universities are strapped for resources (both money and facilities) and may delay in making good on the promises they made in the offer letter, such as assigning lab space shortly after your arrival. While this may be nobody's fault, it is really important that you push gently but incessantly to have the promises kept. For instance, if you are waiting for a lab, find out if there are any spaces that are used rarely or not at all and ask for permission to adapt them. Sharing a lab with another faculty member may be a temporary solution, but make sure it does not count as a permanent solution and does not lower your priority for future consideration. Even though you lack seniority and tenure, it is important to keep pushing until you get what you need. Any feathers you ruffle will be far easier to smooth out than will an inadequate research portfolio down the road. If you are quiet, the assumption is that you have what you need.

Staff support. Do not underestimate the importance of staff for your success as a faculty member. Staff is the glue that holds departments together. This has become painfully obvious now that nationwide budget cuts have resulted in the permanent loss of many staff positions. In my experience, staff members are usually very dedicated and very efficient people who are also overworked and underpaid. Being courteous and respectful toward staff and showing appreciation for the work they do is the least a faculty member can do (for instance, do not expect a staff member to drop everything and immediately work on an assignment just because you waited till the last minute). You will find that many time-consuming things can proceed fairly smoothly if you have an efficient staff person on your side. Also, staff members have the rare perspective of interaction with all the faculty members and can be a valuable source of information on the department climate and politics. Departmental, college, and university-level staff personnel are likely your primary points of contact about how things work, where to have paperwork submitted, payroll, immigration status for foreign faculty, and even procedures for grant submissions and administration of funding awards. Forging good relationships with staff early on is critical.

Support from other faculty. It is likely that you have been hired into a department where faculty members get along with one another for the most part; some interpersonal quarrels may exist, but they are usually not toxic, so as an assistant professor you should be able to stay out of conflicts without having to pick sides. As a junior faculty member, you were most likely brought into the department to strengthen research in an existing area (if the department wanted to start hiring in an area where they currently have no one, a prominent senior hire with a named, endowed chair would have probably been the first hire in that area instead).

There are probably several faculty in your disciplinary subarea who have championed hiring you, and who are your most likely future collaborators and supporters. You will probably closely interact with one or more of these colleagues — which is precisely why they can, in principle, be the most damaging to your tenure case, as close interactions may, in fact, be too close for comfort and lead to competition, irritation, or animosity. Keep your collaborators and allies close, but try to get out of any excessively negative discussion about any of your colleagues.

I am not saying not to trust anyone, but rather to be very, very careful about whom you trust with information that can damage your case. Don't lose perspective that these faculty will be casting a vote on your tenure case, and that due to strong interactions they will have a strong opinion of you, which sometimes may not be as favorable as you think — but will carry a lot of weight, coming from someone believed to know you well. Faculty members are people, with all their virtues and flaws, and some come with oversize but fragile egos. While it is good to be cautious — and I have no doubt scared you out of ever talking with any of your colleagues — you will be encouraged to learn that, in the vast majority of cases, your area colleagues and collaborators are indeed your strongest supporters, and are often the people who will give you the most and the best advice on all issues academic.

Most faculty, apart from your area colleagues and/or your collaborators, will likely start as ambivalent, or as sometimes mildly hostile toward you (if you were hired over a pet candidate in a competing subarea). Depending on the size of your department, these faculty may be many. These people will usually be civil but aloof, and will generally think about you in terms of passing interactions and your progress as documented on your CV. These are the people with whom you should be friendly as you serve on committees together and share an occasional lighthearted joke or commiserate about the administration. These are the people who will likely view your CV in objective terms and will support your getting tenure if your record is strong. Moreover, if you have an opportunity to seek guidance or to collaborate with a leading faculty member in an area of expertise outside your field, grab it. It can be helpful to have an independent ally outside of your subfield to keep your agenda moving ahead.

I recommend that you lay low in terms of department politics in the first few years on the tenure track. Do attend the department faculty meetings, but mostly listen and try to determine the department hierarchy (for example, often the loudest people are not the ones best respected; try to determine who the heavy hitters really are, and who the potentially most difficult ones are).

Department chair. If your department has a rotating department-chair position (where a faculty member serves as chair for several years), it is likely that chair will change once and perhaps even twice between your hiring and your tenure decision. Ideally, the chair is supportive of junior faculty and ensures they are taken care of in terms of facilities and resources, as well as that they have reduced teaching and service loads in the first year or two on the tenure track. Also, the chair ought to make sure that you understand the criteria for promotion and that you are given regular feedback on your progress.

Do your best to build a good and collegial relationship with the current chair as both a colleague and an administrator. You should do your share of service as a junior faculty member, but be aware of what the requirements are for all junior faculty and avoid volunteering too much time and energy to activities that do not directly benefit your tenure case, even if you feel this would get you in the chair's good graces — it likely won't, not in the way that ensures long-term respect for you. Also, be aware that the chair, like any other faculty member, may not necessarily be your friend as he or she may have other, stronger loyalties that predate you. If you feel you are not in the chair's good graces even though you feel you have done nothing wrong, try to be realistic in assessing what the chair's agenda is (with the help of trusted colleagues, if possible) and decide how to strategize around it.

Formal and informal mentoring. Some universities require that a formal mentoring committee be assigned to every assistant professor on the tenure track. Mentoring committees often consist of one or two faculty who are supposed to be the first point of contact for tenure-track faculty when questions regarding teaching, research, or service arise. The committee may be required to meet with the assistant professor to go over the annual progress report, with or without the department chair. You may have a say in who your committee members are, and it is best if they are people you trust. I recommend finding out early the university-mandated and department-mandated types of feedback on your progress, and, if there is any type of mentorship you have a right to, try to have it materialize. Get all the feedback you can.

Sometimes the faculty members on the formal mentoring committee are well intentioned but may be too busy to meet with you when you need them, or you may not be willing to inconvenience them and ask for advice, so they ultimately fail to fulfill their purpose. Luckily, there are usually multiple opportunities for informal mentoring. For instance, excellent mentoring can be provided by your collaborators in other departments, as collaboration keeps the lines of communication open and you can more freely say what's bothering you without it coming back to haunt you at tenure time (of course, gossip travels fast and knows no boundaries between departments, so be cautious whom you trust even outside the department).

If you are a member of a minority group, there may be university-wide mechanisms to have a senior faculty outside your department assigned as a formal mentor. Inquire about this option with human resources or the diversity affairs office. This person can also offer plenty of advice on the workings of the university, and you can share your thoughts and fears relatively freely, as this person will not be casting a vote on your tenure case.

Peer support. Most universities offer introductory/orientation workshops for new faculty. These are great opportunities to meet young faculty from other departments, who will be undergoing the trial by fire in much the same way as you. Some of these people might end up joining the group of your closest friends, as they understand exactly what you are going through while not being your direct competition. I recommend getting involved in these workshops and taking advantage of any later activities that foster interdepartmental peer bonding, such as college-level or university-level junior faculty coffee or lunch meetings. In addition, for minority faculty, there are often support and fellowship groups (e.g., groups reaching out to women in science or to international faculty).

If there is no established infrastructure for this type of support, consider starting your own group with a few kindred spirits. Make it a habit to meet every few weeks or monthly for lunch or drinks after work. At least until tenure, it is certainly less dangerous to complain to a friend from a different department about the annoying Professor Bigshot from your department than it is to give Bigshot a piece of your mind. Do not underestimate the therapeutic powers of camaraderie and commiseration on your well-being and professional success.

Slightly Scary Tenure Stories

There are few things scarier to a newly independent academic than the tenure-case evaluation. The prospect of a tenure case gone wrong for some perverse and unforeseen reason has been known to wake assistant professors up in the middle of the night, drenched in sweat. Being nervous as you are approaching tenure is totally OK; being testy is OK too, just don't call your department chair names, or anything else that's hard to take back. And remove sharp objects from your office. And switch to decaf.

I am a relatively recent survivor of the tenure evaluation process, so here is my contribution to the confusion and panic among tenure-track faculty (mwahahahahaaha!) in the form of two true stories that scared the bejeesus out of me in my fourth and fifth years.

Scary story No. 1

At my institution, people are strongly discouraged from going up for tenure early, and if you want to go up early you have to be significantly better (after the shorter time) than an average person after six years. This actually came up in a bizarre case of a woman who was going up in her sixth year (regular time) but had two children during her tenure track and actually had tenure-stoppage paperwork in her file (a year for each child). The thing with tenure stoppage is that you can use it if you need to, but you don't actually have to use it if you don't need it. This woman clearly did well enough that she didn't feel she needed the extra years. However, there was a smart ass on the university-level promotion committee who said: "Well, her tenure clock has been stopped, so she has really been on the tenure track for four years, therefore she's in fact going up for tenure early and must be *much better than an average sixth-year candidate*." Can you believe that?! Instead of saying, "Good job, two kids didn't slow you down at all!" this person said, "Aha, the kids didn't slow you down, so instead of evaluating you as a normal sixth-year candidate, we will evaluate you according to even harsher criteria reserved only for Trailblazing Superstars." How's that for a reward? Luckily, several reasonable people on the committee stopped the idiocy from hurting the candidate's case.

Scary story No. 2

My institution is very conservative in selecting external letter writers for tenure cases. The candidate must not supply *any* information on the desired letter writers, but he/she is allowed to give one or two names of whom not to include, in case some animosity is involved. The list of letter writers is compiled by a few designated colleagues from the department, and the letter writers should all be members of the National Academies, award winners, endowed chairs at very prominent institutions, and so on. The letter writers are not supposed to be asked whether they are available to write or not before the formal requests are sent out. Simply, a list of names is compiled, letters are solicited, and then you wait. A department will ask for many letters, often more than a dozen, in order to receive at least eight.

I have seen cases where this selection of letter writers without any input from the candidate results in poorly chosen letter writers (e.g., too far from the candidate's area) and too many lukewarm letters ("I've never heard of this person"), which hurts the candidate. I have also seen one single letter sink the case at the university-committee level, where people may not be from the candidate's field and rely heavily on what famous professors says about your work. As an example, I know of a faculty member who raised a lot of money and had some visible publications, but who was denied tenure because a poor selection of the external evaluators resulted in one dismissive and several lukewarm letters. The candidate went up again in his seventh year (by which time he had raised even more money and received some awards) with a completely new dossier and a new set of letters, whose writers were now chosen much more carefully. He sailed smoothly to tenure.

In my experience, the external-letter part of the tenure evaluation process was extremely scary, because it felt completely out of my control, yet I knew the university-level committee would put extraordinary weight on them. On the upside, I do believe that most letter writers really do try to give an honest and objective account of the tenure case at hand. People on the tenure track should definitely do the "tenure tour" near the end of their probationary period. Travel as much as possible, meet as many people who have the potential to evaluate you as you can, and showcase your work in any venue for which it may be appropriate, even if it is not among your favorite conferences. As a bonus, all the extra invited talks at conferences and seminars at universities look good on the CV. I killed myself traveling in my fifth year. It was grueling but I think it was totally worth it.

Traveling without Moving

If I had to point out one aspect of my career that was significantly impaired by having small children, it would be my ability to travel.

About a week after I had defended my PhD, I moved to my shiny new tenure-track faculty position at a big state R1 with my young child. We lived apart from my husband during my first couple of years on the tenure track so he could work on his degree. Traveling was extremely difficult for me during that period because there was no one to take care of my child — dad was 2,000 miles away. Occasionally, my husband would come to visit and care for our child so I could travel, which meant he was taking time off and I would still barely get to see him. These two years were very stressful on our marriage. I was quite busy and quite miserable, and so was my husband; I worked a lot and everything was new — teaching, recruiting students, and writing many, many grants.

After a couple of years on the tenure track, my husband joined us, and shortly thereafter I got pregnant. Owing to pregnancy and breastfeeding, my travel was even more restricted in years three and four of the tenure track. I did go to the most important conferences, breast pump in tow, but traveling minimally is far from leaving no networking stone unturned.

By year five on the tenure track, my academic record looked very good, except that I felt I had not gotten enough exposure. That's when I undertook the "tenure tour," a year of aggressive self-promotion and extensive travel in order to have my work seen and heard, and to try to meet everyone who might potentially be asked to write a letter of evaluation for my tenure case. The travel schedule was grueling. The whole tour was embarrassing in certain ways — I was shamelessly prodding people to invite me to give seminars, and I hosted a large number of senior guest speakers whom I didn't know well enough to wrangle an invitation from for myself. The self-promotion year was quite stressful on my husband and my children. Whenever I left, someone immediately got sick with a fever and either vomiting or diarrhea, so as to maximally gross out my poor husband. It all worked out, and I was approved for tenure smoothly at the very beginning of my sixth year, with what I hear were glowing letters all around.

One significant downside of reduced travel in my field is the reduced funding potential. Most well-funded people in my field have money from one or more of the defense agencies. The thing with defense agencies is that one's potential for funding depends largely on a project's programmatic value to that specific program officer's portfolio; it helps if you know your program officer very well. Therefore, traveling and talking to program officers, making an effort to be on their radar, and establishing a personal connection are critical. I did very minimal fundraising travel on the tenure track and have been reprimanded by a senior collaborator many times for that.

Instead, I have always conducted the work of my group so as to minimize travel and maximize research output per dollar. I can compare my career trajectory with that of a colleague from another, closely related department, who started at the same time as me. The colleague was single, took to travel and fundraising immediately, and drew lots of money. In contrast, I stayed put and was more successful at recruiting and advising students early on, so I had papers from my own new group ready for publication early in year two. The colleague took a significantly longer time than me to successfully recruit students and get output from them, even though the colleague's group grew much more rapidly and there was more money around. Overall, my publication rate with a smaller group was higher than the colleague's and I graduated my first student earlier, but the colleague brought in more dollars to the university than I did.

What's the moral of this story? While I believe that you can do a lot of good science and good advising without burning a lot of jet fuel, you should travel as much as you can. Travel for fundraising, travel for networking, travel for exposure. If you don't, your career will take a hit. It may not be lethal, but it will be damaging. If you have visions of grandeur, efficient fundraising and extensive networking are key, so you better dust off your frequent-flier card. If you choose to be earthbound, or if the choice is temporarily made for you, there is still plenty you can do for your career, but be realistic about the inevitable compromises and sacrifices that you will have to make.

Tenure Denial

Have you ever noticed how certain words or certain phenomena seem never to be on your radar, only to show up repeatedly over a very short time span?

I remember a few years back coming across the word *sinister* (not exactly a word frequently used in daily communication) probably five or six times in a single day from as many different and unrelated sources, only one of which was a Disney cartoon where the adjective qualified a villain. A much more serious example is a particular fetal malformation of which I had previously never heard, only to find out that two women whom I knew ended up losing their babies because of it within a few weeks of one another.

In much the same way, at one point I heard of three cases of tenure denial over a period of just a couple of weeks. My department is low drama in that regard; people get plenty of feedback and generally know if they are doing well or not, so surprises are rare. My own tenure case, while anxiety inducing, was objectively a slam-dunk and got approved unanimously at every level. There were no issues with tenure of the several colleagues who are junior to me, so I sometimes forget that being denied is a very real possibility.

When things look really bad, you can usually see the signs well before tenure. Ideally, the precarious situation is communicated to the junior faculty member early enough that they can decide whether to do something about their performance or choose a different career path. We have had a few people who left after their third-year review, because it was clear that there was little that could be done to change the unfavorable disposition of the department. In two of those cases, the candidates were not listening to advice as to what they should do and decided they knew better. When it becomes clear during your third-year review that not only have you received no grants (that can happen; everyone is aware of the funds getting scarce) but the reason is that you were in fact not applying at all because you had decided it was not important and you focused on research as that's what you wanted to do (I am not making this up) or because you waited for the world's largest amount of ironclad preliminary data to even begin writing, that's a really, *really* big problem.

That's how you don't get your contract renewed after a third-year review.

In contrast, all three cases of tenure denial that I came across recently (research schools, different physical-science fields) were borderline. In each case, the decision could have justifiably gone the other way, but it is not clear that the departments made a mistake, i.e., I could see why they wanted to deny tenure. All three candidates had independent funding and had published, but less than optimally. One had issues with equipment, which is very unfortunate, and a corresponding publication gap late on the tenure track. Another had very few publications, and while the field is such that the publication rate is not high and the candidate ultimately published some very high-impact work, it was simply too little, too late for when the tenure dossier was submitted and I presume that, as far as the tenure-case letter writers were concerned, the record was really weak.

The tenure track is short. You cannot embark on a single lofty goal during this period. If you really want to do far-reaching, high-risk work, you absolutely have to balance it out with shorter-term, sure-payoff projects. The papers that will count have to be published by the end of year five on the tenure track, and ideally earlier, so that there's enough time for people to come across your work. I have seen more than one case where the all-eggs-in-one-basket approach ended up backfiring: even though the seminal finding was eventually published somewhere prestigious, it was too late for tenure.

The tenure track is as much about strategizing, "career engineering" if you will, as it is about ideas and technical execution. You have to learn the job fast enough and show others that you know how to do it, that you can raise money, teach, advise students, publish papers and give talks, and make a name for yourself — on time. The tenure track is usually not the time to devote all your energy to a project you have always wanted to do; do it only if you can balance it with something else, otherwise leave it for after tenure. Many people do their best work post-tenure anyway — the key is to do what you need to do to actually get tenure first.

How Much Is Enough for Tenure?

I had an email exchange with a colleague from a different university and a related field. He is new to the tenure track and is facing the common and aggravating vagueness in people's responses when trying to find out what the tenure criteria at his place actually are. Of course, he knows he needs to bring in grant money, publish, teach, and do service. He also knows that, since he's at a major research university, teaching and service have to be decent, but not earth-shattering.

In his situation, research is the key to succeeding or failing on the tenure track, but what about some concrete metrics? *How much money is enough? How many papers (per year or perhaps cumulatively over the duration of the tenure track) are enough?*

These criteria depend on the type of place you are at, the field, and how your department ranks overall. I can speak of the criteria at my place, which is a large state R1. In the physical sciences and engineering, we have several top-10 departments and I think all others are in the top 20. (I don't follow the ranking of the biomedical fields, but we have a medical school and my understanding is that the biomedical sciences at my place are very good. But I don't know enough about their criteria for promotion in terms of money brought in or publications.) So what follows holds in the physical sciences.

The number of papers obviously depends on the number of group members you have, but I would say the dependence is somewhat complex. Some people say that it's as many papers per year as you have group members — presumably, the new ones don't publish, but the more senior ones publish more than a paper per year, so it roughly comes out right. I have actually found that the number of papers I typically publish (these are comprehensive papers in archival journals; I don't count conference proceedings) is roughly five to seven per year. This has been the number for me since my second or third year on the tenure track, when I had four grad students, as well as right after tenure, with one postdoc and eight students. When the group is smaller, I have more time to work on my own and spend less time chasing money, so some of these publications are single author or I am actually doing the technical work for a collaborator (as opposed to delegating to a student). When my group is on the large side, I have to raise much more money to maintain it, meaning I spend much more time writing grants. I also spend much more time advising all these students (weekly one-on-one meetings take more time). Overall, at some point more students stops meaning more papers; the number of papers per year as a function of increasing group size flattens and eventually starts to drop—you don't want to be in that regime! I have a very successful senior collaborator whose group always has 20-something people, of which probably five are postdocs at any point in time. He churns out 10 papers per year, but they are all very high impact. That works for him, but it is not the only option. I can say I am quite happy with the size and composition of my group — large enough for a diversity of projects and for group meetings to be meaningful, staggered well to maintain continuity, but small enough (especially in terms of how many newbies I have at any point) to be manageable and resilient to funding fluctuations.

Which brings me to how much money you need to raise. It depends on how money hungry the powers that be are. My dean loves good fundraisers, especially if you have large requirements in terms of space and equipment. Perhaps the best advice I received was: "You need to raise enough money to sustain a viable research group." I have seen people go after money for money's sake and their group swelled to more than they could manage and then eventually imploded quite spectacularly. You don't want to go from a 25-person lab to a three-person lab over the course of one semester (true story), firing multiple techs and postdocs because all funding fountains dried up at the same time. It's important to realize what it is that you want to be doing, how many people you need (this may take a little while to figure out), and then get the money to do it. Under the assumption that you have an idea how large the group should be to do what you envision, the money you need equals the annual financial support for all the group members + summer salary for yourself + equipment + materials, supplies, and travel (say, two conferences per year per group member other than yourself), all with fringe benefits, overhead, and tuition where applicable. You should perhaps aim to get a bit more, but once you have enough you should be able to allow yourself to exit the grant-writing mode for a semester or perhaps even a year, and simply do the work you promised to do.

So, how much *is* enough? The best way to estimate how much money someone has is by their group size. I have heard numbers of about $1 million to $2 million at tenure time to be considered respectable, a sign you know how to write proposals. Obviously, experimentalists have to raise more than theorists, and of course this number scales with the group size, but it seems these numbers are universally thought of as "nothing to sneeze at."

In terms of papers, go look at the records of recently tenured faculty in your field at comparable or better places, and see how many they have per year. At my place, the number 20 or more papers from your group at tenure time keeps coming up. I think that's a good estimate. Papers with your former advisor's group don't count for much, in my experience, and I was strongly advised to sever ties with my former group as soon as possible after starting on the tenure track.

Ultimately, the external letters of evaluation will put your standing in the context of your field and your career stage, so you want to be among the better ones of your cohort. You don't want the letters to say "Candidate is worse than A, B, and C, who all got tenure at comparable places." You want them to say, "Candidate is on par with (or better than!) A, B, and C who got tenure at comparable places." Or better yet, "Candidate walks on water, then turns said water into wine, and has left A, B, and C from comparable institutions so far in the dust that they are all still recovering from a coughing fit."

Collaborations on the Tenure Track

When you are being put up for promotion to associate professor
with tenure, your record is subject to intense scrutiny (tenure
review). Typically, this happens in your sixth year, but depending
on the school, the department, and your record, you may be put
up a year or even two earlier, or even a few years later, often
because of tenure-clock extensions for family reasons. At many
universities, early promotions are rare.

The most important part of your tenure package at research
universities is — shockingly! — your research, as evidenced
primarily by your publications, grants, and awards. In addition to
the total research output, the composition of your papers is
important, too. Your research output (papers in journals and/or
conferences) is supposed to resemble a food pyramid: lots of
fruits, vegetables, and grains (your own group's papers), a fair
amount of lean protein (collaborations you have established while
on tenure track), fats and sweets only sparingly (papers with
former advisor(s)). A majority should be your own group's
papers, with the lead senior author (typically listed last in the
author list) being you and the lead junior author (typically listed
first) being your student or postdoc. Generally, if your intellectual
offspring is first author, it's considered *your* paper.

The tricky part is collaborations. Your external letter writers —
people who are supposed to assess your work and ideally know it
well, but often don't — will be asked to evaluate your
contribution to the field, which also means evaluating how much
you contributed to your collaborative efforts. Sometimes this can
be quite hard to do, particularly when people's areas of expertise
overlap. Junior faculty are in danger of not being assertive enough
on collaborations with senior faculty (here I assume it's not your

former advisors, but one or more collaborators that you teamed up with while on the tenure track), and two things often happen: (a) you have a senior collaborator on some of your papers for what are more-or-less courtesy reasons, they did not contribute tremendously or are peripheral to the paper, but won't remove themselves from the author list and you are uncomfortable removing them yourself; (b) the senior collaborator is always last author, whether warranted or not.

Either way, you run the risk of your good, hard work being associated solely with the most senior or most famous person in the author list. This will certainly happen if they occupy the lead-senior-author position, but often even if they don't (this happened to me), because, owing to their fame, their name is already in people's minds and thus most easily associated with a piece of work. So be proactive about removing courtesy co-authors (I know, it's unethical to even put them on unless they contributed significantly, but junior people often feel they owe stuff to senior people so these co-authorships tend to linger). I recommend being open about it: "Dr. Famous, you know I am on the tenure track, and we have done some nice work together, but as I am sure you know, people will be trying to judge my own contribution, so I would like to pursue this line of work where my contribution will be unambiguous and separated from your work."

To avoid having your collaborative work associated with the more prominent senior collaborators, make sure people know what *you* have contributed. Talk to anyone willing to listen about the great work that you are doing, and insist on being credited explicitly in the talks given by your senior collaborators; usually people will do it on their own, but you never know. Also, traveling on the tenure track to give talks is very important, so people can get to know you. If you start having children while on the tenure track, you may have to cut back temporarily, but try to at least do the "tenure tour" — usually a fifth-year tour where you try to go and visit most of the places where letter writers for your tenure case are likely to be chosen from. (You may need to "invite" yourself to some of those places: see "Traveling without Moving" for my own story of this tour.)

Another thing that must be done is weaning yourself from your former advisor(s). It is OK to wrap up the papers you still have unfinished from your previous position, but this collaboration should not continue past a year or two on the tenure track. I had a talk very early on with my former advisor, in which I said I was expected to cut him off. He said no problem and we agreed on which paper would be our last together.

When the time comes to write your research statement (a typical part of a tenure package), make sure you can succinctly say what it is that you and your group did as part of every collaboration.

Collaborations are a means of creating some — if not all! — of the best science around; they can be lots of fun and truly inspirational. To the university, collaborative papers show that you can play well with other kids. Just make sure the other kids don't get the credit that's rightfully yours.

Tenure, for Better or for Worse

There are very good employment opportunities in industry for a person with my scientific background. My PhD students, fresh out of grad school, get starting salaries in industry comparable to what mine is now, and that's without bonuses or stock options. I don't see their employers discarding them carelessly, because industry needs good people with specialized skills, and these people are not common. Quality PhDs are not expendable, at least not in my field. Since professors are paid significantly less than their industry counterparts, yes, to sweeten the deal and actually get people to work in academia, you need to offer job security.

Being a faculty member at a research university never stops being a rat race. We have annual review and evaluation, based on which salary increases are calculated. If you do poorly, you don't get a raise. If you don't bring in research money or publish papers, you must teach more than those who do. Also, every tenured professor has a big review every five years, so there is some quality control in place. People retire after having advised and funded students for over 30 years, still having federal grants.

I also do not know of a single tenured woman who turned into deadwood due to childbearing. If research productivity suffers at all, it's for no more than a few months. Most of the time, tenured academic women have established research programs that run uninterrupted during their absence, so you would not even see a glitch in their research records due to childbearing. As for being absent from teaching and advising, many women take no time off. Those who do, do extra work beforehand or after they come back, or arrange for colleague coverage, a favor they return later.

I hate it when I read opinions that basically state that academia — a multi-decade commitment for academics — should never make any accommodation for anyone's life challenges. God forbid any academic, male or female, should be allowed to temporarily slow down for a birth, death, or illness in the family.

I have several colleagues who have gotten seriously and irreversibly ill on the tenure track or shortly thereafter, largely because of the stress. We all have colleagues who ended up divorced or have forsaken having kids altogether because of professional demands. No job deserves this kind of personal sacrifice without something pretty major in return. In the case of academia, that something is tenure.

You only really want to tenure those people who will not slow down significantly or permanently after they receive tenure, i.e., you want to tenure the people who have the fire in the belly that drives them to excel irrespective of external stimuli. People who are truly ambitious and passionate about their work. People who have worked their hardest toward developing their research program and are not just going to drop it and let it die away.

But then you don't really need tenure, do you? If these awesome people are the only ones you want to tenure, and they will keep chugging along and never stop, they don't care about or need the protection of tenure, right? Tenure is just for lazy people, right?

Wrong! Why? Because 30 years is a long time, and life happens.

A friend of mine is launching a start-up after several years at a major corporation. He's a young and unattached guy with a PhD and a lot of spunk, who can put in all the hours needed to launch a start-up, and that's exactly what he's doing right now. He says he would not be doing it if he had a family.

Another friend of mine, a lawyer, works for a district attorney's office in another state. She used to work on cases that were extremely high-profile and stressful, and required long hours. Then she got married and had a child and decided to move to a different division, where she can still do her job but with less stress, and she has more control over her schedule.

What I am trying to emphasize is that, in most careers, highly trained people are able to change jobs or to adjust their work hours and schedule to suit their life's demands. In large companies, there may be opportunities for lateral transfers, and in some fields, people can even adopt a part-time schedule for a while without derailing their overall career. None of these are available for academics. It is very rare for faculty to go part time because of the stigma of not being serious enough. Moving laterally within the university is not possible because there is no such thing as a less stressful faculty position at a research school.

The tenure track is like dating, while tenure is like a marriage between the university and the faculty member: for better or for worse, in sickness and in health, till retirement do us part. Most academics will spend the bulk of their independent career at a single institution. While on the tenure track, just like while dating, assistant professors try perhaps a little bit harder to please the object of their affection than they do after receiving tenure. But, ultimately, the relationship is doomed to fail if it's based on incompatibility or pretense, so a long dating period is advisable. Six years (the duration of a typical tenure clock) is a pretty long time to *pretend* to be ambitious, work your butt off, and convince everybody around you (your department, university, and professional community) that you love your work, are genuinely driven, and have something unique to contribute to science and to your university. The bottom line is that a person's real ambition and abilities do come across fairly accurately on the tenure track.

This committed relationship between a faculty member and a university typically lasts for over three decades, during which the faculty's children are born, parents get sick and die, and the winds of change in research-funding availability blow every which way. If an academic is supposed to put all these years of work into a university, the university should show comparable commitment during the faculty member's trying personal times. Tenure, like marriage, shows the world that the cute couple — the academic and the university — are both in it for the long haul.

Ride It Like You Stole It

Impostor syndrome refers to feeling like a fraud (despite objective evidence to the contrary), feeling like you have no idea what you are doing and therefore don't deserve the job or award/promotion/congratulations/cookie, that you instead lucked out and stumbled/dropped/slipped on a banana peel then fell into the undeserved, coveted "it," that any minute now someone is going to discover your true shouldn't-be-there-anyway colors, and take it all away.

Impostor syndrome seems to be quite common in highly competitive fields. In the fields with a drastic overrepresentation of a certain race or gender, people from underrepresented groups suffer from the syndrome virtually by default. It appears to be quite common among academics, and many women and minority academics in STEM suffer from it. Let's say you have impostor syndrome. From experience, I can tell you that it may lessen over time, but it's probably never going away. So, instead of wishing you didn't have it, it's best to focus on finding ways to be productive nonetheless; how to go about it differs with career stage.

I have been a professor for over a decade. I feel less like an impostor now than I did while I was on the tenure track. The feeling was initially sort of justified, in that I really didn't know how to do the job; nobody really does when they first start out. But that's not being an impostor; that's just being a baby academic. The tenure track is brutal and the learning curve is pretty steep.

At some point, I realized that I would never be rid of feeling like an impostor, but along the way I have learned to muffle the nagging voice and not let it block me, not let it prevent me from doing what I wanted to do for extended periods of time. I still have very down-in-the-dumps days, which are best dealt with by going home early. The impostor syndrome likely impedes my achievement somewhat; without it I'd likely do more or do better work or whatever, but the point is I don't think it will ever go away, and I have accepted that. I think we spend a lot of time discussing how it's unfair that some people feel it and all the ways in which it hinders them. But there is no point in lamenting what would happen if I didn't feel like an impostor. I do feel like one, and that's that, but with experience I have found ways to work around it and just get stuff done. We get hung up on this romantic ideal that a person should feel free and unencumbered by doubts while doing their academic work, otherwise they are doing it all wrong and should be doing something else instead. Yet, most adults do boring and uninspiring jobs for a living, and I would take my academic job, with big dollops of self-doubt, over pretty much any other job in the world, any day of the week. So I just focus, really hard, on getting things done. Feeling happy about myself is not a requirement for getting stuff done. I know how to do this job, so I can do it even when doubting myself. Doing leads to accomplishments, and then I feel good for a millisecond, or three. Then it's on to the next thing anyway.

For me, working with students really helps with impostor syndrome. Sometimes I get a really nasty paper or proposal review, then feel down and ask what the point is and who cares and whether I am really stupid or uninspired. And I feel like crap for a few days. But I have students and I cannot be too down for them. They expect me to have my act together and to know what we will do next, and to tell them that we will revise and resubmit and that things will work out well. For them, I act as if I do have my act together; I go through the motions, imitating someone who does have their act together, and in going through the motions, in faking it, I actually do get things done and things do eventually work out.

However, this is me after years of experience. *How do you fight feeling like a fraud while you are still new and relatively inexperienced, while you are on the tenure track?*

So you fear you don't have what it takes, that you shouldn't be in your tenure-track position, that you have somehow managed to fool numerous astute people over many years about your abilities. (Of course, in reality, all the people who have been writing recommendation letters for you, and all the people who interviewed and hired you are not stupid. Nobody is into charitable hiring. If you don't believe in yourself, believe in their judgement. They would not have hired you if they didn't think you had what it took.) But let's say you did fool everyone, what's the worst that could happen? What is it that you fear? That somebody, *everybody*, will discover you are a fraud? Well then, since you are headed for certain ruin and disrepute, you could curl up into a ball and not do any work and ensure that the doubt becomes a self-fulfilling prophecy, or you could make the time before they inevitably find you out count, right?

Let's say you don't really deserve to be here. *So what?* That's life, people get things they don't deserve, good and bad, *all the time*. Are you going to give your job back? Of course not, don't be stupid. You don't actually owe it to anybody supposedly more meritorious to give up your position, no matter how many schmucks on the Internet say that women or minorities have it soooo easy because their jobs are due to quotas and affirmative action. Even if what the schmucks are saying were true, that still doesn't mean that any of them are in fact entitled to or even worthy of your job, no matter what they think or what they want you to think. This is *your* tenure-track job now, *you* got it, end of story.

You have this amazing opportunity to be your own boss and do science with smart young people, pursuing any direction you like (the definition of "like" being "can get extramural funding for"). Yet you feel unworthy, apparently believing that the job belongs to someone else, someone more worthy? *So then ride that tenure-track job like you stole it, because you sure feel like you did.* Hold onto it with both hands, scream loudly so everyone can hear you about how fuckin' ecstatic you are to have it, and work as hard as you possibly can because it is such an amazing gift. Work with wild abandon, because if it's true that you are not meant to be there, they will come and kick you out, so you might as well make what little time you have count.

And in working like there's no tomorrow, you will accomplish things, and the accomplishments will slowly but surely loosen the grip that the little voice has on you, even if it never goes away.

Chapter 4

Teaching and Service

What Makes a Good Teacher?

People who work in education have precise metrics for what effective teaching means. I am not an education scholar, but I do teach and doing it well is important to me. In my view, there are roughly three important facets of traditional teaching: the performance art of teaching, the one-on-one or small-group interactions with students (discussions, office hours, email correspondence), and the course materials (including exams).

The performance art of teaching is also known as "being good in the classroom," being charming and engaging, being able to convey your own knowledge clearly and effectively. At research universities, some of the best in-class teachers-performers are also among the best-funded, most successful researchers. This should come as no surprise, as the ability to explain and engage are as important when impressing a panel of grant reviewers as when trying to animate sleepy undergrads in a morning class. Being an interesting lecturer correlates strongly with good teaching evaluations: students highly value being engaged. This aspect of teaching is also one that comes much more easily to some faculty than others; for those who are naturally charismatic presenters, it doesn't take much time or effort to mesmerize the crowd.

The second part is individual or small-group interactions. The "flipped" classroom (see below) strives to eliminate the lecture in favor of small-group interactions that follow out-of-class viewing of videos. In a traditional classroom, these may be office hours or a discussion section. Small-group interactions are very beneficial to student learning, but many students don't take advantage of them. Holding frequent office hours, for instance, where only one or two students show up, requires a lot of professorial time, but likely has a very small effect on teaching evaluations, even though it can be extremely helpful for those who show up. Also, spending a lot of time on email is one of those things that everyone expects from a professor, so you will likely be penalized in evaluations if you don't do it, but won't be praised if you do.

Finally, there are the course materials. In my opinion, good course materials (I include exams in this category, as a good exam is not just a test, but an educational opportunity) are critical for student learning and require considerable time to create. One type of course material I do not create is slides. These days, many people teach with PowerPoint slides (lovingly abbreviated as PPTs); it works for some, perhaps many people, so kudos to the readers for whom it does. I appreciate that PPTs take a lot of time to make, so the effort is not lost on me. But I always hated PPT lectures as a student, as they always made me fall asleep. The teachers who worked with PPTs alone generally didn't move from the lectern, which further made everything static and my narcoleptic self would just doze off. Personally, I like to work on the board; I find that working on the board helps me pace the lecture, so the students can more easily take notes. That and my tendency to move around the classroom seem to keep them awake.

Good homework assignments and projects, which really bring key concepts into focus and enforce what was done in class, are hard to develop. In my view, this is exactly the most important part of learning for the students, because they don't really retain anything until they try to apply what they think they grasped in the lecture to actual, specific problems. That's where they see they didn't get all they thought they did. However, copious or difficult materials that really lead to learning are not necessarily widely appreciated by students, especially not in the short term, i.e., not on the timescale relevant for student evaluations.

Some of the best lecturers I have had didn't end up teaching me much in the long run. The lectures were breezy and fun, but the breeze and fun came at the cost of rigor and substance. On the other hand, some of the people I learned the most from were pretty boring in the classroom, but the materials that we had to go through really worked for me and made me learn. Of course, it is quite possible and perhaps not even rare to have a teacher who is both charismatic in the classroom and a master project/homework creator. My absolutely best teacher ever was the author of a beloved textbook classic. He was magnificent in the classroom — not what you would call charismatic, but still strangely captivating — and he gave the best, most interesting tests I have ever had in my life; they profoundly affected how I design my exams today. I remember loving his courses and looking forward to his brain-teasing tests; most of the graduate student populace dreaded them as tricky.

Sometimes people say that great teaching doesn't require a lot of time. I would say that great *lecturing* probably doesn't require a lot of time. I can work an undergraduate classroom quite effectively with minimal preparation. While a traditional lecture with an enticing teacher is where interest might be sparked, learning doesn't happen until the students themselves do the work.

A good teacher inspires a student to want to put in the work and learn; a *great* teacher organizes the course and makes the materials such that even the students who are not inspired end up learning the essentials, in spite of themselves.

Flipping the ~~Bird~~ Classroom

The powers that be have recently started encouraging us to adopt "novel, paradigm-shifting teaching strategies" specifically the "flipped" classroom. While I don't necessarily think it's a bad idea, the zeal with which the concept is being pushed is making me want to dig in my heels in protest and never change anything.

The presumably right-side-up, traditional classroom involves a teacher who lectures and students who do homework outside of class. In the upside-down, flipped classroom, students first view prerecorded lectures and perhaps do some quizzes before coming to class, and class time is used to work on homework problems and other active-learning materials.

Whether it makes sense to flip a classroom really depends on the discipline, the type of course that is being taught, as well as the class size and level (e.g., undergrad freshman courses are different from graduate ones). In many STEM fields, undergraduate courses have discussion sections in which a teaching assistant (TA) helps the students with the homework problems. To me, the great administrative love for the flipped classroom seems a little too much like another creative way to cut costs: get rid of the TAs and have the professor do the TA/tutoring job. Interestingly, nobody is mentioning any tuition reduction.

There is no doubt that I am a priori uncomfortable with the prospect of a drastic change in teaching largely because it is a drastic change. Perhaps a modification is necessary because things are broken, somewhere, somehow, or could simply be improved. But I don't really see a reason to change things just to change something. I am an experienced teacher and have practices that work well and keep the students engaged and learning, so I am unconvinced that a "paradigm shift" is entirely necessary. Students are not failing; they are doing reasonably well. They could do better, which means we should probably think about slight rather than revolutionary shifts in how we educate them.

In STEM, someone needs to explain the concepts to you or you need to read the book, ideally both, and then you need to work on problem sets. Nothing can really replace the deliberate practice that a student gets by doing the homework problems. We can make the problems more fun, but if we are serious about teaching, then the students have to do the work. Perhaps by flipping the classroom we are somehow trying to make this work seem painless, because it's not done at home, alone, but rather in class, with the instructor. I am not sure that's possible; as the saying goes: no pain, no gain. Moreover, homework problem sets in STEM fields often take considerable time to do, more than the 150 minutes per week that a typical three-credit course would allot for the homework-in-class activity; students would still need to work at home.

With a flipped classroom, considerable work needs to be put in by the instructor ahead of time in order to record all the lectures. I talk fast, so I am sure many students would appreciate being able to go back and rewind my lectures; this point is not lost on me. However, I am really uncomfortable with the prospect of my lectures being recorded for posterity; I make silly jokes and generally goof around with students to add a bit of levity to class, but I am not sure I would be crazy about my performance being freely shared on the web. I really like the ephemeral aspect of teaching; the lecture is a fleeting performance, always unique. I don't think I have ever taught things in the exact same way twice — with different students in class, the pace is different, they ask different questions, and the experience is never exactly the same. I really love that aspect of teaching in a lecture format.

For many students, close interaction with the instructor is key; that's why massive open online courses (MOOCs) will never be a substitute for the college experience, although I think they can supplement it. While many people learn well from others and really benefit from enhanced interactions with teachers and peers, there are students whose learning may actually be inhibited by this practice. When you, as a teacher, ask a question in a lecture, usually a handful of students responds. The number increases as the course progresses and as you actively try to include other students. Still, there will always be students who don't want to engage. Some are just not interested. Some are not following; these students would likely need additional help. Some are interested and following just fine, even doing great in the course; they are just not the type who likes to engage. I believe that too much interaction in the classroom can actually be quite torturous and even counterproductive for introverted types.

When I was a student, I always appreciated a good lecture. For me, the lecture was the first prompt, the efficient first introduction to the material, and the chance to hear concepts laid out with a clear emphasis on what's important. During the lecture I would listen, take it all in, and then process everything on my own. I personally don't think I would have liked *at all* constantly having to interact with the teacher, or peers for that matter. And can we say "bias"? I am not sure that women and minorities in the fields where they are underrepresented necessarily benefit from increased exposure to either the teacher (who grades them!) or other classmates while being in the trying-to-get-things, working-on-homework state. Imagine all the added opportunities to be told how "Girls can't do math"!

There is something I don't doubt, though: frequent assignments and frequent refreshers, such as quizzes, do wonders to keep the students continuously working and overall aid in the retention of the course material. There are great ways to use technology to create online assignments and quizzes that help achieve this goal. Also, I think the students should be given ample opportunities to interact with the instructor, and then take it or leave it. For instance, the instructor can help by holding multiple office hours, perhaps in a classroom if the office is too small. When I teach undergraduate classes, I have six or seven people in my office (pretty much full to capacity) at any given time during office hours; if you are approachable and available, students will come find you if they need you.

Instead of the traditional or flipped classroom, how about a "buffet classroom"? Offer the students a number of options for interaction (lectures, frequent office hours, discussions with the TA, email, forums) and let the students take what they will. Top it off with carefully crafted assignments and tests (paper and online), and finish with a dollop of simply caring.

HIGHER EGGUCATION

Grouchy Musings on Teaching

I have issues with some of the advanced teaching strategies as I see them implemented in my department. (Flipped classroom, I am looking at you, and all other "eggcellent" paradigms.)

My main complaint is that the responsibility to sit down and understand the material and work until proficiency is achieved is being taken away from students and moved entirely to instructors. Instead of the students taking ownership for their own learning, we the instructors are supposed to devise lectures to be tutoring sessions (the flipped classroom model), so the students don't have to think about the material alone at home. But working alone is the only way you really learn! Instead, we hold their hands while they work through problem sets, smoothing out the kinks as they go along, misleading the students into believing that the road to problem-solving is easier than it really is. I have seen some unimpressive products of flipped classroom instruction, as the students come to my class with an A in a prerequisite that was taught in a flipped format, and they don't understand anything; they certainly can't do any relevant problems that they hadn't specifically seen before. We try to remove the natural and necessary discomfort that comes from learning, being challenged, being required to stretch beyond where we are. And this incessant insistence on everything being with other people, like flipped classrooms and group projects, is an introvert's nightmare. Can't we please let people think in peace?

These new techniques are completely opposite to my own teaching philosophy. I, as the instructor, need to be there to help when help is needed, but the student has to think and grapple with the material alone *first*; this is absolutely key. Ideally, this is the sequence: Come to class, read the book (or the other way around), start on the homework early and on your own, do as much as you can on your own; then ask a friend/come to discussion/come to office hours *after* you have thought about the problems on your own really hard, because by then you will be sensitized to what you are missing and what you don't know, and therefore much better at remembering explanations and clarifications. Instead, I see many students work in packs, with a pack leader who's a strong student. The rest contribute little, but still feel very good about their command of the material; studying in packs works well for their grades, as long as homework and projects carry a lot of weight in the final grade. But, an exam setting shows how much each individual knows, and the students can get surprised by how little that may be.

Another aspect that I am very tired of is students constantly asking that we only teach them the practical stuff that will get them a job and none of the useless abstract crap, presumably because at the age of 19 or 20 they know exactly what it is that they will or won't ever use. Employers want what they want, and most don't want to pay for it; they want a new graduate to come trained in all the minutiae that the employer (any employer!) could possibly want. Employers have no qualms about wanting universities to act as trade schools, which is not what they are or what they should be.

Sure, we should provide training in the latest and greatest tools and techniques, because I agree that our students should be employable upon graduation. However, what peeves me is how joyously these kids rush toward becoming corporate cogs today, without stopping to think what will keep them employed 20–30 years from now. Why? *Because the jobs that exist today didn't exist 30 years ago.* The only way you remain competitive for STEM jobs over the long term is if you have a good, solid base in many basic sciences (for the physical sciences, that's first and foremost math, then physics, chemistry, computer science, statistics ...) as well as in writing and speaking. The stronger and wider your base, the more able you will be to change careers if needed.

I do my part, but I wish we were collectively better at communicating to our students that our task as educators is not to just ensure they get their first job out of college, but to give them the knowledge base and the self-study skills that will keep them nimble, growing, learning, and ultimately employable throughout their lives.

GRADING NECESSITIES

Quixotic Grading Dreams

In the school system that I went through, graded homework was basically nonexistent — I stopped having homework assignments in the fourth grade. After that, there were lectures (you needed to take good notes) and textbooks to learn from. For math and physics, there were books of problems, and you were supposed to go through them and practice in order to do well on the exams. It was similar in my undergraduate program: there were traditional lectures and discussion sections, the latter where the TA would do typical problems with us. Still, there was no homework, just books of problems, and it was up to us to study and practice in order to do well.

When I came to the US for grad school, I actually liked the fact that there was homework in graduate courses. Turning in homework weekly or biweekly forced me to study the material at a regular pace (I couldn't goof off and then cram before the test), which meant that preparing for exams was trivial and took no time at all. I also liked that there were term papers and projects, which I had never had before.

Then I became a professor and started having to grade.

What I dislike is that unless the homework is graded students will not do it at all. Especially at the undergraduate level, students have beautiful, colorful textbooks, full of examples and problems, yet few students would even think of doing any problems other than those assigned for homework. This is totally mind-boggling to me. I had a student a couple of years ago come ask me what he could do to prepare for the next exam, as he hadn't done so well on the previous one. I said the minimum is to read the lecture notes, review his own in-class notes (students here take very few notes, which is another thing I just cannot wrap my head around; most sit and listen with their arms across their chests), read the book, and go over all the homework problems in detail, asking himself what it is that each problem actually emphasizes. He said he wanted more, and I said sure, by all means, do all the problems in the textbook, but he didn't find this to be an appealing option; he wanted me to select the extra problems for him to do.

I love assigning term papers and projects, and I don't mind grading them. They are substantial chunks of work, requiring students to synthesize multiple concepts and deliver a meatier result, but they are of most use in upper-level undergrad or graduate courses. The common week-by-week homework is really just for the students' benefit. So many of them copy from each other, or from previous generations if you recycle any problems, that it's pointless to grade this work. Sure, you can assign very little value to each homework assignment, but someone still has to grade the whole thing. Either some poor graduate student spends many hours every week grading undergraduate homework assignments or I have to do it. No matter how little homework counts for, the time needed to grade it is the same.

This is what I would ideally like to see regarding grading (I am talking about physical-science fields here): I assign homework every week, with a due date, and right after the due date I post the solutions. Most homework assignments are not graded, but students take the responsibility for their education and do them anyway because it's good practice of their craft. Then there would be a few assignments, e.g., involving programming or calculating something complicated, that would be turned in and graded (the percentage of these would be higher in upper-level undergrad or grad courses). I could also assign some larger projects and/or term papers that I would collect and score, and they would count for a nontrivial percentage of the final grade.

The point is, I don't want someone to have to waste time on grading trivial practice problems that the students should do in order to gain a basic level of proficiency, problems that can be (and are) easily copied and thus count for little. I would like to see more student ownership of their own performance in the course, and them ready to put in the time to practice, without necessarily every minute of their time actually counting for a grade. (I hate the "But I worked so hard! I put in so much time!" pleas for a higher grade. I want to see what you learned, not just that you put in some time.)

Bimodal

I talked with a senior colleague a couple of weeks ago and he mentioned that grade distributions have become increasingly bimodal. There are the kids with high scores and the kids with very low scores, and very few students in between. The colleague said it didn't used to be like that, that the students 20–30 years ago were simply better on average, and grade distributions followed the beloved normal (Gaussian) distributions.

I don't know how students used to be, but I can attest that the bimodal distribution is the norm rather than the exception in many of my courses. There are the students who are obviously getting the material and who could probably take on even more challenge. And then there are the kids who are so far behind and who have so many deficiencies from lower-level courses that it's unclear what it is that they are actually getting from the class, if anything.

The problem with this profile is that you don't know at whom to aim your lectures. My best-ever teacher in grad school said "20 percent of the students will do great no matter how poorly you teach, 20 percent will do poorly no matter how well you teach, but there are 60 percent of students where how you teach really affects what they learn and how well they do; you want to tailor your lectures toward the 60 percent." However, I see 40 percent who are doing well and 40 percent who are doing really poorly, and 20 percent who are doing so-so. The people who are consistently doing really poorly likely shouldn't even be in this major, but I don't know what to do about it. Because of them, I can't do what I could with the students who are doing really well. Rather than a near-continuum of abilities, we have a pretty big chasm, such that most of the class is either really bored or really lost. It seems that there are very few people near the average, for whom the middle-centric approach of my former teacher would work.

What I do is try to assign extra homework with some brain teasers for additional credit, and two to three extra problems per exam that require a little non-trivial thinking. The lectures do still get dragged toward the lowest common denominator, which leaves some kids really bored. I am not sure how to teach to a class with such a wide range of skills. Ideally, the students at the very bottom of the curve would get sent back to take some remedial courses, but I can't see that being a widely acceptable practice, as college costs a lot and everyone is interested in funneling the students all the way through to a degree, somehow, as fast as possible. We as teachers are encouraged to find a way to pass students, but then the value of the good students' bachelor's degrees drops with every poor student who has graduated despite having learned very little.

Who is the one who tells a student, "Maybe this is not a major for you" or "You need to go back and learn some calculus and then re-take the class"? What is best for the student may not be what is best for the enrollment numbers on which department budgets hinge. Consequently, we go soft on the people who really should not be getting our degrees. I try to mind my own business and I am no rebel, but this issue makes me wish I were. It makes me sick that everything is always only about money, and that even our core mission — educating students — has to deteriorate for this reason.

WHAT PROFESSORS WISH WERE ACCEPTABLE RESPONSES TO RIDICULOUS STUDENT REQUESTS

On Classroom Teaching

I don't think I have always thought this, but I suppose I do now: you can, in fact, be a good researcher and be an atrocious teacher. And I don't mean being bad because you don't prepare or otherwise blow off your duties. You can put in the work, you can care, and you can still suck.

I have a colleague who is brilliant, but he has a breathtaking inability to put himself in other people's shoes. I have known him for years, so I have learned how to talk with him and get the information I want, but it's quite amazing how little he grasps the viewpoint of his conversational partners, and what they know or care to hear about. I think he has no idea how he comes across or that what he is saying is making little impact. My colleague is representative of a small but memorable group; like his brethren, he talks to everyone as if they are in his head, privy to every detail of the thought process. This is an affliction from which many a graduate student presenter suffers, but it's usually temporary and curable. Alas, for some, it's congenital and the prognosis is grim.

The colleague cares about the students in his classes and about his teaching, and he gets frustrated, year after year, when he finds yet again in evaluations that students really dislike him. I don't know what to tell him — he's senior to me, and he's a good person and a good scientist, but I can totally tell why he is not clicking with his students. Half the time I can barely follow his train of thought. I wonder if anyone ever told him point blank what the issue was.

I had another colleague who was similar — he was terrible at telling jokes, because he'd start from the middle or assume the audience knew something that they didn't. He would crack himself up with his comedic attempts, but everyone else would be left confused.

Most of us at universities don't get any formal training in teaching; we just work at it, pick up tricks along the way, and hopefully improve with practice. But I guess an ingredient that is necessary is some level of empathy or perhaps emotional intelligence — being aware of the audience, of what they know, and then having the ability to meet them where they are. Can this skill be taught? Probably. But it's probably also true that some people do it naturally and others don't. And I suppose there are some who are naturally just very, very bad at gauging where other people are, so without training they go on sucking (and suffering) in the classroom.

On Classroom Teaching, Part Deux

The university requires annual peer reviews of teaching for assistant professors, so yesterday I did a review for one of my junior colleagues. I went to one of his lectures (he knew I was coming), took notes, and I will write up a report for his tenure file. When I was an assistant professor, most of my reviewers would meet with me after the lecture to chat about their impressions, which I thought was nice and collegial and anxiety reducing, so I did it, too, after yesterday's review.

This was a large undergraduate class with more math than many students can comfortably take in, and the colleague is a junior faculty member teaching the material for the first time to an audience considerably more populous than he'd ever faced before. He did well and will certainly get better with practice.

Between yesterday and today I got to thinking about how much one can actually really improve and if there are aspects of one's personality that just cannot and should not be curbed in teaching. For instance, I sometimes get comments on evaluations that I speak too fast. That is probably true, perhaps even to a high degree. When I was an assistant professor, I tried to speak more slowly, but it adversely affected my delivery: I was too self-conscious and so focused on my speech speed that it took away from my focus on the content and on student questions. So I stopped trying to change; I talk how I talk.

If you consider teaching evaluations as a useful metric for teaching, mine went up somewhere during year three or four on the tenure track, from initially being about 84–86 percent of the maximal score as obtained from about a dozen questions (department average over all faculty is around 75 percent) to being consistently around 94–96 percent, even when I teach large undergraduate courses; I occasionally get 98 or 100 percent with grad courses. Some of the improvement had to do with confidence — accepting my own style for what it is, trying to be myself when teaching, and thereby reclaiming the fun rather than pretending to be someone else. But much had to do with adjusting the content and delivery to better suit the average student I actually had in the classroom, rather than, well, I guess a clone of me. Here is what helped the most with my teaching, especially of undergrads:

- Distill the material. Cover fewer topics, but cover them really well. Spend enough time on the most important concepts, relentlessly emphasize things that are critical, and explain why and how they underscore the overarching ideas about the field as a whole. When something is just a parenthetical remark or a diverting tidbit, say so. There is value in digressions and side information, as they provide color and a change of pace, but be absolutely clear about what is IMPORTANT, what is Important, what is important, and what is not really all that important but is cute or fun or curious, or a chance to make a pun and wake up sleepy students 55 minutes into a 75-minute lecture.

- Make course materials that highlight what you need highlighted. I am not a big believer in online recordings of lectures. The world does not need me to be yet another talking head, delivering elementary content online. I believe in doing examples/problems/projects and in choosing or creating assignments that tackle the core concepts from different angles, so that something will end up working for (almost) every student. I like to assign small computational projects that result in the students making plots or videos, or I even give them chunks of code they can tweak and produce something audible or visual. If I am using a nonstandard format in homework for a specific purpose, I tell them in the homework setup why I am doing it, what I want them to focus on, and what I expect them to get out of it.

- Explicitly draw connections to topics covered in other courses. This also requires teaching broadly across the curriculum and perhaps getting involved with student advising so you'd know what they hear in other courses, when, and why. The best students draw these connections themselves; to the rest, it makes a huge difference when you explicitly point out what to pay attention to and why, how it relates to their overall educational goals and interests, and where else they may have seen the concepts already.

- Office hours are useful for students and for you, and can be great fun. The only way to learn where your teaching is working (or not) or where your students' preparation is adequate (or not) is from the students. So give them ample chance to interact with you; the baseline is having office hours. As my experience with teaching increased, so did my ability to get the students to ask questions in class and to come to office hours. Having more office hours is not necessarily better if they are not properly scheduled. Choose due dates for homework so they are not on a Monday (because students will then work over the weekend, when they can't come ask for help). Organize office hours so you are available before the deadline. Increase availability before the exam.

- Your personality is your personality, and you should work with it and not against it. If you love cracking jokes, go for it. If you are serious, by all means be serious. In teaching people to teach, there are overarching tenets that are centered on students and on learning: Focus on proper content and on clarity, emphasize the really important concepts, and engage not just the students' ears but their eyes and minds and hands with assignments. Be kind, patient, and available. But the rest — how you go about fulfilling these requirements, the minutiae of content delivery, mannerisms — should be left up to the teacher. There is no one true style; it's not something that can or should be taught, anyway. The teacher's unique personality is a key ingredient in successful learning.

The colleague I reviewed is a smart and knowledgeable guy. He is also serious and to the point; one of the reasons we hired him was that he showed lots of technical substance and creativity, without fluff. For the same reasons, I don't see him becoming the charismatic beloved teacher that some of my colleagues are, seamlessly interweaving lecture content and anecdotes about their kids. And he shouldn't have to; there should be space for serious people in the lecture hall, people who are kind and patient, but not necessarily vaudeville performers.

Serves You Right

(Originally appeared in Inside Higher Ed)

Research, teaching, and service are the defining trinity of a university professor's job. Their relative importance depends on the type of academic institution and one's career stage. Understanding how to strike a balance between institutional requirements and one's own career interests can sometimes be tricky, and young faculty are often in danger of overcommitting to activities that do not benefit their long-term career prospects.

Most tenure and promotion criteria at universities state something like, "In order to receive tenure, a candidate must demonstrate excellence in research, teaching, and service." In reality, this means that excellence in research is absolutely mandatory for promotion and the level of excellence you achieve is in direct correlation with how easily you will get tenure. Provided your research record is spotless (i.e., you received a lot of external funding if you are in a science discipline or another where that's the norm, published many papers in top journals or books with respected publishers), you graduated some PhD students, and you gave many invited talks, the university will be fine with good teaching and adequate service. It doesn't work the other way: excellent teaching or service do not get you promoted in the absence of a stellar research program. Bad teaching may result in tenure denial, though.

But can't you have an outstanding research record, as well as outstanding teaching and outstanding service? The answer is, "Yes, in principle." The problem is that, if you are devoting too much time and showing too much zeal toward either teaching or service at a large research university, your colleagues will wonder what it is that you are not doing instead, i.e., why you are not spending all this time on research.

While the quality of research and teaching can in principle be measured — through the number of papers or the amount of grant money or teaching evaluations — service is a vaguely defined category that has the potential to drain a junior faculty's energy, with poor return.

What is service and how much service is enough?

Service is a set of faculty duties that demonstrates good citizenship in the department, university, and broader scientific community. Therefore, we can roughly divide service into service to your institution and professional service to your scholarly community.

Service to the institution can be further divided into departmental service and service outside the department. Departmental service requires a fair bit of time, and it includes serving on various committees (e.g., undergraduate and graduate student admissions, facilities, curriculum, student advising), serving on students' master's and PhD defense committees, or serving in an administrative capacity (e.g., being chair). Service to the university outside the department also involves being elected to serve on various committees, but these are often open to tenured faculty only. On the tenure track, it is reasonable to assume that most of your service to the university will be to your home department.

Professional service to the broader scholarly community comprises activities such as reviewing research papers, serving on the editorial boards of journals, serving on organizing and program committees of conferences, mail-in and panel reviews of grant proposals, as well as serving on the board of a professional society or a federal funding agency.

The level of department and university service for a junior faculty member should be fairly light. I recommend that most service activities be skewed toward professional activities in your broader disciplinary community, which, besides being service, have the additional benefit of enhancing your research program and your visibility. For instance, reviewing papers enables you to stay abreast of the latest developments in the broader field, being part of technical program committees for conferences gives you visibility and enhances your network, and serving on grant panel reviews strengthens your ties with program managers and helps you feel where the field is moving.

Find out what the absolute minimum of service is that the department requires and stick with that. Often, this means you will serve on one committee, and try to pick one that you either feel passionate about (e.g., facilities or curriculum planning) or one that does not require a lot of time. If you are really passionate about serving your institution, I advise that you somewhat curb the passion until after tenure. Try not to commit to more than one additional committee in excess of the required minimum. Serving on the master's and PhD defense committees for your colleagues' students is extra, and these will help strengthen your bonds to the faculty in your subarea; however, these activities should also be practiced in moderation.

Sometimes, junior faculty feel that they owe it to someone to put in excessive amounts of service. The reasons differ: For instance, women are sometimes pushed into extra committee roles because committees need gender diversity, or it is perceived that all women like service because they are stereotypically nurturing and caring. If you are female, and even if you love service and happen to be nurturing, I recommend that you fight tooth and nail not to perform any more service than your male counterparts. This will not only free up your time, but will also establish that you are not a pushover, which is important for your future standing in the department.

Another example is when a junior faculty member feels vulnerable, such as when he or she is the trailing spouse in a spousal hire, or when the hire is a member of a minority group and thinks people will perceive him or her as a beneficiary of affirmative action. In these situations, some tenured faculty feel the new hire is not really meritorious and the new hire often feels that he or she needs to perform extra service in order to get into the colleagues' good graces and demonstrate goodwill. If you are in this situation, the worst thing you can do is pile on all the extra service tasks; not only will this course of action detract from your research and result in confirming naysayers' doubts, but it also makes you seem insecure and hungry for approval and will only exacerbate any ill will the colleagues may harbor toward you. I know this is hard, but you have to keep telling yourself that you have as much right to your faculty position as anybody else and that you do not owe anybody anything above and beyond what every other tenure-track faculty does. Be friendly and civil and do your share, but be firm and protect your boundaries.

In general, while on the tenure track at a university, it is a good idea to be a little selfish. Your goal is to get tenure, and that means the primary focus is developing your research program and the secondary one is honing your teaching skills. Regarding service on the tenure track, find out the minimal requirements for an assistant professor in your department. Stay close to that minimum for the duration of the tenure track, even if you burn with desire to serve more. Instead, devote more time to professional service that brings visibility to your work and enhances your research program and funding prospects. If any free time opens up after trimming unnecessary commitments, spend it with your family and recharge. Once you have secured tenure, you will have plenty of opportunities to take on additional service roles and engage more deeply in faculty governance at your institution.

Not Your Emergency

I once chaired a search committee. Owing to various reasons outside the committee's powers, we had an extremely short clock: a little less than three weeks from the application deadline to the expected time to produce the short list. Then we needed to start interviewing right away. These three weeks overlapped with major holidays, which means we could not get access to many applications because the staff person in charge was taking time off, and we can't expect staff to work when not at the office. So we had a week to make the first cut, a week that included a second major holiday and during which all our staff were off, too, but never you mind, because faculty work nonstop anyway. So we made the first cut and sent out for letters of recommendation with a fairly short turnaround time, while apologizing profusely. By the way, I was the one who spent several hours in the afternoon and evening customizing and emailing all these requests because the staff person who would normally send these out could/would not do it till the week after, and we didn't have the time to wait. Most letter writers seemed to be fine with this request and promptly emailed their letters. But then I get this email from one professor, scolding me for such a short turnaround time and telling me that other places give four to six weeks for letters (the requested letter was attached anyway).

Well, bite me. No, I have not been sitting on my hands, if that's what you are implying.

All faculty are perpetually in the putting-out-fires mode, and most of the time it's not because we are lazy or disorganized. It's because we are constantly being pulled in different directions and often have to prioritize other people's immediate needs over those of our groups. Last semester, I spent a lot of time reviewing all sorts of internal proposals and award nominations for a university-level committee, sometimes during inopportune times when I really needed to work on something else. Often there are proposal deadlines, project-report deadlines, all sorts of administrative and service deadlines. And I am not even talking about the deadlines that appear because one of your collaborators finally got their head above water and can finish the collaborative paper they've been sitting on for months and only has a week before another pile of crap befalls them, so of course, if you want this thing to get done, for your own sake and the sake of all the students and postdocs involved, you drop everything else and make sure this paper gets out.

I am constantly putting out fires that weren't started by me. It is very annoying and one of the most stressful parts of the job. As a result, the aspects of the job that are the most important in the long run — working on science with group members and looking at their papers, as opposed to, e.g., refereeing those of others —

get postponed. I don't think I am unusually bad at deflecting the crapola flying my way from all directions. I try to protect my time, but no amount of careful prioritizing and scheduling helps prevent all the deadline-driven work dropped in your lap by others, who are also likely getting ruffed up by someone else to do stuff last minute.

Near as I can tell, all faculty fight this battle, and it is simply part of the job. It gets much, much worse after tenure. That's why it angers me so much when I see that a fellow scientist feels it's their duty to scold me for asking for a short turnaround time on a letter of recommendation. They should know better than to assume I am a disorganized twat or the whole committee isn't doing their job, and, instead of admonishing me via email, simply take it as yet another request that needs to be done on a suboptimal timeline, likely sent by an equally stressed-out colleague from another institution.

Real and Surreal Academic Work

At universities like mine, doing research is prioritized in every way imaginable over teaching and even more so over service. However, all these "lowly" activities that are subservient to research still have to be done by someone, generally a faculty member, and they take both time and energy. Teaching involves prepping for a new course, class time, creating homework and writing up solutions, creating exams, grading, and office hours. Service: I was an undergrad advisor last year, I sat on a very fun but very demanding university-level committee that selects projects for intramural funding, and I also chaired the department's search committee. And let's not forget the review of papers and proposals, as well as participation on funding panels and technical program committees of conferences. Owing to rapidly declining institutional support, there is also a massive amount of secretarial work that faculty now do. I spent two hours yesterday filing reimbursement forms for my recent trips. The work is not hard and the online system is pretty well done, but there are many details that have to be looked up and entered (e.g., electronic ticket number for each flight, reimbursement record number for the conference registration I had previously filed). I also have duties pertinent to managing my grants, including some paperwork related to funding and travel reimbursement for graduate students.

I admit I have fallen prey to the pervasive sentiment that all time not spent on research is wasted, that it doesn't count as work at all. This attitude has really been bringing me down on many levels: I can easily spend a full, fast-paced day teaching, meeting with students, grading, having committee meetings, and reviewing papers, and at the end of the day I am exhausted, yet I feel like I have wasted the whole day and haven't done anything at all. Then, instead of taking a break in the evening, I try to make up for lost time and do "real" work, and as a result I never have any time to just unwind.

I have decided that I am going to start counting this "surreal" work as real, bona fide work. I have decided that, at the end of a day I spent doing massive amounts of teaching or service, I will pat myself on the back and say, "Good job! You deserve to rest," and actually crack a book or watch a show in the evening, then go to bed at a reasonable hour, instead of fighting to stay awake to get a little more done.

Many people seem to think that embracing all aspects of professorial work is a path to becoming "deadwood," irrelevant on the research scene. ("Real scientists don't waste time working on degree-program accreditation! They spend their time in Washington, DC, schmoozing with program managers.") All I know is that I am tired of working my butt off, yet always feeling like a failure because it's not "real" work, the kind that counts. Sure, it would be great if we had more secretarial support or if being an excellent teacher actually counted for something, or if all the time I spend reviewing other people's papers and filling out travel reimbursements did something for my own career. But, they don't, and wishing doesn't make it so. So either I stop doing all this "surreal work" (I know people who are so negligent of all non-research duties that I don't understand why they work at a university at all), which my sense of duty wouldn't allow, or I decide that they are worth doing and are part of my job anyway and that I will not feel bad all the time for doing them.

Chapter 5

Grant Proposals and Funding

Grant Proposals: Love 'Em, Hate 'Em

When I think about grant proposals, I am reminded of a very good friend of mine whose pastime is building custom-configuration computers; he really enjoys it and is very good at it. I asked him why he doesn't try to cash in on it or at least go into some type of consulting, because he seems lukewarm about his actual job and very passionate about the pastime. He answered along the lines of "It's only fun as long as it's a hobby. It would no longer be fun if I actually *had* to do it to get paid."

For an academic scientist or engineer, writing grants would be the most enjoyable thing in the world if only it weren't so darn important to actually get the money.

When you think about it, writing a proposal means you get to immerse yourself in the literature, learn a lot of new things, ask exciting and far-reaching questions, brainstorm, dream big, and distill your ideas through writing. As a bonus, writing a proposal gives you an excuse to drop all menial work and cancel all unnecessary meetings without feeling guilty, because everyone leaves you alone when you say, "I have a proposal deadline." For me, writing a grant is a guilt-free exile into what I love best — research.

But ...

One's career and the livelihood of one's students and postdocs hinges on success in getting grants. Funding rates are depressingly low; in my division at the NSF, the funding rate is roughly 10 percent. An average faculty member writes a large number of grants to get one funded. Of course, I am not assuming that grant awards are completely stochastic — we all know to correlate merit with fundability — but the number of grants that are competitive is several times larger than the number of funded ones. There just isn't enough money to fund all solid, promising work.

I remember how helpless one feels on the tenure track before getting that first grant. The world of funding agencies seems unpredictable and hostile, and you wonder how far and how thin you can stretch those start-up funds. Even after you have received a few grants, the world of funding agencies remains unpredictable and hostile. You keep writing proposals because you have to support your smart and hardworking group members and the money you seemingly just received is already running out. I am not sure why some faculty cease to write grants post-tenure, but I don't think it's because they are not driven. My guess is that it has to do with the disillusionment and hopelessness after too many rejections, as the wells of funding in certain fields dry up.

I think the only way to keep doing it — writing many, many grant proposals — is to savor the pleasant, creative parts and try to minimize the damage to your soul by the unpleasant parts (also known as being declined). If a person finds absolutely no enjoyment in the proposal-writing process, having a faculty position in the sciences or engineering will be a rough ordeal.

Who's on Your Proposal?

There are several types of proposals, based on the structure and the number of co-principal investigators (co-PIs) involved. They come with different time commitments for the principal investigator (PI), as well as different levels of frustration and types of challenges during preparation.

1) The single-investigator proposal. This type of proposal is by far the most work for the PI, but you have total control over the idea, the timeline for execution, and every word and figure that makes it into the proposal. If a single-investigator proposal gets funded, the money is all yours, and usually there is a fair bit of flexibility in how you distribute it (depending on the funding agency). But, if you get bad reviews, it's all on you and it's hard not to take it personally.

I love single-investigator proposals because I don't have to compromise; it's nice to sometimes just have everything 100 percent my way. Ideally, I come up with an idea that excites me and then write a proposal. Successfully conveying this excitement in writing helps you find a champion on the panel. The single-investigator proposals where you are literally in love with the project are certainly the most enjoyable ones to write, but it does sting twice as badly if the panel says negative things about your "precious."

2) A collaborative proposal with another PI. These grants can be very enjoyable to write, as you get to share the workload with another person, there is built-in feedback on your writing, but you presumably still have a fair bit of control over the outcome. That is, unless the other person is considerably more egomaniacal than the average academic.

3) The small-group proposal (typically three to six people). These are, in my experience, the most common type of multi-investigator proposals. You end up having two or three people who do the lion's share of the writing, with the rest contributing significantly less. The composition of the team is key for success — I have had successful previous proposals of this type, and it's always with people whom I know well and whose areas of expertise complement one another.

4) The multi-investigator, large-center proposal. These proposals involve dozens of co-principal investigators (co-PIs), organized into groups of about 10. These are a pain overall and really hard to get funded. The amount of text each co-PI contributes is fairly small and it's really hard to turn these nuggets into a coherent effort. The people who are the group leads have to herd the cats and have to produce something cogent out of the hodgepodge of write-ups.

Center proposals are very difficult to put together — months of meetings, brainstorming, inviting and disinviting PIs, trying to create a team from a group of near strangers. Such massive efforts are usually led by the Big Cheez. You can actually spot a future

Big Cheez (or a Big-Cheez wannabe) as a person under the age of 50 who wants to take on such a monstrous task.

NSF CAREER Tips

The NSF offers prestigious CAREER awards, five-year grants that are meant to enable promising young faculty to develop their research programs. These awards are on the order of $500,000, but the size varies somewhat with division and directorate. Depending on your school's overhead and your lab needs, this usually won't cover much more than lab supplies, one graduate student, and one month of summer salary per year. But, the prestige associated with CAREER is significant, and getting it is a valuable (although certainly not necessary) ingredient in securing tenure. CAREERs are typically due mid-July. Here, I will try to provide a discipline-independent set of suggestions for writing this type of grant, based on my experiences as a former recipient.

1. Getting Informed

As with all grants, contacting the program director is extremely important. Typically, not all program directors in your division will be involved in the CAREER program. So, first find out who the cognizant program director is for CAREER and contact him/her early on, before you start writing. April or May is early enough that they may not be entirely swamped yet.

Some divisions utilize mail-in review, some do panels, and some combine them (panels in addition to mail-in review). In some divisions, CAREER panels are composed of prominent senior faculty; in others you can have recent awardees. The review type, panel composition, and program director may be significantly different from your regular experience, so get informed early. You may need to be persistent in trying to get a hold of the program director, but it is very important to do so.

2. Scope

CAREER grants are different in scope than regular NSF grants. They are painted with broader strokes, you are allowed to dream bigger, more far-reaching dreams in the CAREER than a regular three-year grant. After all, CAREER is supposed to establish a foundation for a lifetime of achievement (paraphrased from how I remember the solicitation). I interpret this as the following: What is it that you would most like to do in the next 10 years? Write a proposal on the first five years of *that* project. A project of too narrow a scope is not appropriate for CAREER. If you have a nifty idea that potentially opens a new niche where you will be a star, that's the type of project you want for CAREER. Once you have the idea formulated, run it by the program director. If you have a few ideas and don't know which one to write about, run them by the program director. The helpful ones will say, "This one is too narrow; this one is appropriate."

3. Readability

As always with panel reviews, the writing style should be such that a panelist reading your proposal in the middle of the night before the review, after having travelled all day and having read several more proposals on the way, still gets a clear idea of what it is that you want to do, and why it's exciting and important. In CAREER proposals, you are more constrained in terms of space than with standard grants: there is a 15-page limit, as usual, but you should devote a much larger chunk to Broader Impacts (about five pages, more on this below), so count on having only 10 pages to demonstrate the vision for your career development, to describe the idea and the execution plan, and to detail how the project helps you long term. As a result, you may not be able to get excessively technical. Readability is key. I am personally also partial to short titles, but people vary on this issue.

4. Broader Impacts (BIs)

This part is extremely important in CAREER grants. While the BIs for a standard NSF grant would be about two or three pages, for CAREER this section is typically around five pages. Many people think "education and outreach" when BIs are mentioned. While these are not synonymous, that is what I will start off with.

For a standard grant, activities such as the inclusion of undergrads in research and plugging into your institution's existing initiatives on broadening participation may be sufficient. (Saying you'll advise grad students and disseminate results in journals doesn't cut it even for a standard grant; it's implicit you will do that anyway.)

For CAREER, you have to go beyond this minimum and show some creativity. You don't want the education part to look like an afterthought, but as a natural outcome of your research. For instance, introducing a new course or augmenting an existing one with your proposed work would be a nice ingredient of your BIs. Maybe you want to interface with local teachers to create K–12 modules that relate to your research. Try to be creative in whom you target: K–12 or the community in the broader sense? Regional, statewide, or nationwide? Specific adult age groups? Specific community organizations (neighborhood associations, churches)? Will you use web resources to access your audience, or perhaps newspapers, radio, or TV instead? Have you made connections with the relevant news outlets, schools, museums? Be specific in your plans.

Your broader impacts need not be limited to education and outreach. For instance, if you propose to cure the common cold or male-pattern baldness, then you should definitely emphasize the societal impact that your work will have and how you can help maximize it through utilizing existing institutional, regional, national, and NSF-funded resources.

Broadening participation is another important aspect of BIs: is there a dearth of women or minorities in your field? Can you find creative ways to target any of these groups through research-related initiatives? Are there ethnic groups indigenous to your region, where you could make an impact? If there are already diversity programs (NSF funded or not) on your campus, explore how you can leverage them in your BIs.

Showing that you have thought how you'll support your BI activities is important, so budget for them in your CAREER grant, if necessary. Be aware that certain components of the BIs are eligible for extra funding: every year you can apply for Research Experiences for Undergrads (REU) and Research Experiences for Teachers (RET) supplemental funds to support the participation of an undergrad or a teacher in the lab over the summer. (There are also REU site grants, but these are something different.) Your institution may or may not have an REU site, but you are eligible for REU/RET supplements to your own NSF grants, and CAREER is no exception. How hard it is to get an REU or RET supplement depends on the NSF division — in some it's a virtual guarantee; in others it's very competitive. Your program director can tell you with how much certainty you can count on these supplemental funds. If they are easy to get in your division, I recommend you mention in your grant that you will be seeking these supplements in the coming years, rather than budget for them in the CAREER grant directly.

Propose what you would actually enjoy doing for BIs. People vary widely in how much time they are willing to invest in the BI activities, so don't propose something you would hate doing, because it shows when you write.

Finally, the BIs should enhance and complement your awesome research, not be a crutch. A great BI section will not compensate for a less-than-stellar research project.

5. Letters of Support

CAREER is a single-investigator grant. However, it is quite likely that you need other people's expertise or the use of someone else's equipment for some part of the project. In that case, every such person should provide a letter of support (where they say they are excited about working with you, but need no money and are separately funded). These letters are included as part of your application under "Supplementary Documents."

I recommend including letters of support for your BI activities as well (e.g., from the principal of the school if you will do K–12 outreach, from organizations/programs with which you will interface for community outreach or to recruit minority students).

Letters of support show that you have thought about these initiatives seriously and made connections in advance.

Good luck!

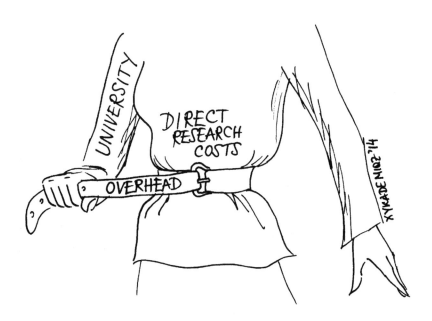

Academoneya

I work in an applied field among the physical sciences at a research institution. My department is very diverse, which has helped me appreciate the challenges faced by the colleagues whose research topics and work styles are very different from mine. One aspect in which we may differ greatly from one another is how much extramural funding we need to raise in order to keep our research programs going. For instance, there are colleagues who have very small groups, zero to two people other than themselves. They operate much like the people in pure math/theoretical physics/some areas of computer science and, perhaps surprisingly, quite similarly to many of our colleagues in the humanities: they do the technical work themselves and usually publish as the sole author. They have modest needs for extramural funds, generally to cover summer salary and travel, and because they work with only one or two students, they are able to give each student a lot of attention. The students might also publish alone, without the advisor as a co-author, and are generally funded as teaching assistants.

My research group is usually 6–10 people, a midsize team for my general discipline — larger than what most theorists or mathematicians have, but on par with many experimental groups. For me, 10 is probably the maximum number at which I can keep track of what everyone is doing technically, make sure the papers are edited and submitted in a timely fashion, and have everyone progress as they should toward graduation. I usually have about four active grants. Some colleagues must raise more money than me in order to support the same number of group members, because their research is more expensive: facilities and user fees, as well as materials and supplies, carry a considerable cost.

Then there are colleagues who have groups of 20–30 people. The management portion of their work is substantial; it is not a small feat being able to organize the work done by so many. It is an even greater feat keeping such a large operation continuously funded. These faculty easily have 15 grants active at any given point in time. Considering that a typical grant lasts three years, that's roughly five successful applications every year. Running a large group is immensely stressful and, on top of technical prowess and vision, requires the level of people skills that grace successful managers and politicians and are somewhat rare among traditional academics. These qualities are unapologetically recognized as important in industry — the fabled "real world" — yet some academics reach for the smelling salts at the mention of people skills, salesmanship, granstmanship, or networking.

Running a midsize research group, like mine, is akin to being a small-business owner. You are responsible for raising the money, supervision of every aspect of the project execution, and dissemination ("the selling") of your products. A benefit of being at a university and working with students is that you don't have to think about their retirement and health benefits (the latter generally come with their assistantships). Having an even larger group brings you into the realm of a midsize business: you start having administrative assistants and technicians and a hierarchy of middle managers, and may not interact frequently with every one of your employees. You also have many more obligations in terms of schmoozing with donors.

We can argue about who's supposed to pay for research and we can all lament the federal science budgets, but the simple truth is that, whether we like it or not, doing research is expensive. Nobody bats an eyelash when people in industry say the same thing — you want something done, it requires manpower and materials. Unfortunately, the large, well-funded R&D industrial labs that used to do fundamental research in the physical sciences no longer exist and everything has moved to universities. Yet, money remains a somewhat dirty concept in academia and there is even a bit of distrust in the people who are successful fundraisers, as if they are moneyed wolves in real academics' clothing.

Much of the divide between the well funded and the rest is the fault of the administration, as the big fundraisers are lauded and rewarded, whereas whole disciplines are derided as a waste of money. The public eats it all up, thinking of some fields as more or less worthy of existing based on the perceived earning potential in the corporate world. At least we academics don't have to fall for it and should appreciate that different fields need different work styles, that this is exactly how it should be, and that academia needs to have a place for all areas of human inquiry.

Writing in a Time Crunch

Some time ago, I received a sizeable single-investigator grant from a federal agency. The submission was in response to a special solicitation with a preproposal, and they reviewed both the preproposal and the proposal very quickly. Between the full-proposal encouragement notice and its due date, I had a fairly short time to write the grant.

The proposal deadline also came at the most inopportune of times, just weeks before a conference that I was organizing. Even if I were to cancel all research-group and collaborative meetings for a couple of weeks, I still had to work on the conference website, logistics, questions from attendees, catering issues ... and listen to the dry runs of my own students' talks. None of this boded well for focusing on the complex technical task of writing a proposal on a very short timescale.

I caught myself panicking, with heart palpitations and shortness of breath, thinking there was no way I was going to finish by the deadline. I was unable to focus, unable to get anything done, paralyzed by the sheer enormity of the task. This grant was based on my previous attempts, and I had received enough feedback on it, but even beyond these criticisms I knew something significant had to change. I could tell it did not quite have that special spark that it really needed to have in order to get funded. Something was missing. In some ways, writing over an old text is harder than writing from scratch, as you keep thinking that you have finished more than you really have and keep getting lured into the old lines of thought. I couldn't just scrap everything (references!) because the turnaround time was so short, yet I had to cut and rewrite quite a bit of it in order to clarify my ideas and present a more compelling proposal.

So I did what I should probably do much more often. Each day, I would write down what I would do in great detail; I partitioned each daily assignment into very small bits, like, "30 minutes to clean up figures 6 and 7 and finish subsection 2.3." When it comes to my work, I have serious perfectionist tendencies that usually make it hard to simply finish things and not go back to endlessly tweak them. I can usually indulge my work-related perfectionism to a point, but this time I had to really curb it in order to make the deadline. For instance, once section 2.3 was done, it was absolutely not to be touched again until the scheduled next-to-last read-through.

Crossing off bite-sized tasks and not going back helped dissipate much of the anxiety and really calmed me down. The fact that this micro-scheduling works is probably not news to people who work well with lists, but I am not one of them. For me, lists are usually more pain than they are worth, but this particular version helped.

While I was writing this proposal, I felt like a horse with blinders on (or at least how I envision a horse with blinders would feel): I kept taking deep breaths, telling myself to just focus on the small task before me, that nothing else mattered. Just redo that figure. Just write three new paragraphs and enter those five references and be done with the subsection. I was amazed at how much progress I was making (and how low my blood pressure was becoming).

This is a story with a happy ending, perhaps because there was a real deadline before me. It's much harder to implement the partitioning and strict scheduling (and much easier to get distracted) with open-ended projects, such as writing a paper.

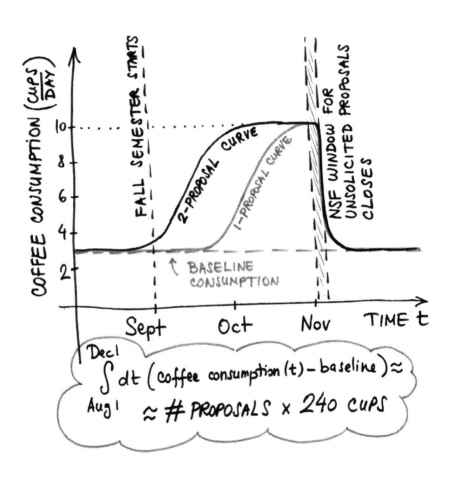

Proposal Review Silliness

There is a game I sometimes play with myself while reviewing proposals, called, "Guess how many grants the PI already has based solely on flipping through the proposal to see the formatting." The correlation is quite pronounced: people who have a reader-friendly layout are universally better funded than those who don't. When you start reading, you also see that their text flows better, even if the ideas are not necessarily earth-shattering and they end up not funded. Successful grant writers care about all aspects of readability, and good, reader-friendly layout is a key part. It helps your reviewer think happy thoughts, as opposed to hate you with a passion after reading two pages because the gray walls of text gave them a claustrophobia attack.

These tips have been mentioned online many times, but they never get old: For goodness' sake, put some space between paragraphs, go with line spacing that's greater than single (1.1 is good), and break up the text. Ideally, each page will have a figure, a table, or at the very least one or two displayed (as opposed to inline) equations. I am a fan of Times New Roman; it's a classic font and you will never go wrong with it. There are people who like sans serif fonts like Helvetica or Arial, which are just not my cup of tea. But if a funding agency says a font is fine, have fun with it.

I know people will say "But I am constrained to 15 (or however many) pages. I can't waste space on silly tricks." Yes, you can and you should. You can purge the fluff, become more clear and succinct, and the reviewer will be happier for it.

Here are some more grant-writing tips:

- Do give your proposal a title that is short and catchy, but please make sure that you are first accurate and descriptive. I reviewed several proposals roughly titled, "Pie in the Sky Is High But I Can Fly," of which one was about the aeronautical engineering of taking off, another was about optimizing the sugar-to-flour ratio in pie recipes, and the third was about why the sky is blue. Based on the catchy titles alone, you would think that these were topically much closer to one another than they were. A good title should not mislead about the contents.

- There are always fads. Once a topic is established as hot, money gets thrown at it, and many people move into the field. However, big groups move faster, and if there are low-hanging fruits, they will be picked by the most nimble. If you are a junior faculty member who is just starting out, with a student or two, you will *not* beat a big-named guy who has invented the field, already has multimillion-dollar centers funding him to do the work, and has an army of minions going after the easy pickings. At best, you'll be just another "me too." At worst, you will never get any money to do what you are proposing, because groups much bigger and much farther along than you got funded to do that exact same thing last year or the year before.

- When you are just starting out, be mindful of what your strengths are and how fast you can conceivably do something. If you are phenomenally successful at getting money and able to grow much faster than an average new professor, then sure, go ahead, go toe to toe with the big guys. But if you are not, then you need to find a niche, something you can do better than others, because of your expertise or how you approach the problems, or because no one else has recognized that some specific aspect may be both important and doable. You need something that is uniquely yours, not just an obvious question within the latest flavor-of-the-week topic. Be realistic about what you can pull off with the money and personnel you have. Once you identify your niche, jump on it with all you've got.

- I laughed out loud in my office at a sentence in someone's proposal that said something like, "In year n of the project, the results will be published in a journal of impact factor at least 10."

AHAHAHAHAHA! Only 10? Why, the stuff is guaranteed to get into *Nature*! Seriously now, that's just amateurish. I can forgive when a graduate student lists 10 papers "in preparation" or "to be submitted to *Nature Progeny*" on their CV, but a grown-up scientist should know better. You can tell me you expect high-impact stuff, but better yet write your proposal in such a compelling fashion that it is crystal clear to me that this will be high-impact stuff, in which case I will strongly advocate for funding you. In contrast, the silly silliness of "We'll *totally* publish in a Super Duper Journal" is just silly.

Funding Dread

Periods in which I spend considerable time either on panels or reviewing proposals leave me filled with dread and despair at the thought of all the effort I need to put into my own grant writing and out of which very little, if anything, will likely come. I am not a very confident proposal writer, which is a bad thing to be when the ability to write strong, persuasive proposals makes or breaks one's career. This is where suffering from the Dunning-Kruger effect (overestimating one's competence largely because of actual incompetence) instead of impostor syndrome would come in handy.

During my panel excursions, I often came across proposals of people who are very well funded. Most of them turn out, unsurprisingly, to be very good and persuasive proposal writers. Even when they don't get the money, when their ideas are only halfway formed, they still write compellingly and are generally ranked near the top of any proposal roster.

Most proposals I review are incremental. People are doing their thing and want to continue doing their thing; who can blame them? There are a few PIs who want to do something out of the norm, but these proposals are usually slammed as "too speculative" and as having "not enough preliminary data." On the other end are the proposals that have so much preliminary data that "they have already done the work" or "it is not clear where the novelty lies." I am postulating that it is, in fact, fundamentally impossible to have exactly the right amount of preliminary data.

So what are the criteria that *do* get you funded by NSF panels? Honestly, it is largely a crapshoot and that's what's so demoralizing. You need to put forth a really strong proposal, but everyone else does this, too. Then you have to be lucky and well placed on a panel. If you are reviewed by a panel where the people are not experts in your field, sure, they can gloss over some technical minutiae where the experts would kill your ideas, but you still won't get funded because no one will champion you. The fate of your proposal is decided in the first 15–20 minutes of a panel review, when the manager goes around the room and asks each panelist which proposal they consider to be the strongest and most worthy of funding. Basically, everyone gets to suggest their favorite and the funded ones are nearly always from among that list. If you are no one's favorite, you are toast. The only scenario in which you might rise to the top is if people tear each other's favorites to shreds, and then you come out as the underdog against whom nobody has anything really damning to say. This rarely happens.

I get anxious just thinking about upcoming proposal writing. I usually have two or three potential topics in mind. Are they earth-shattering? Probably not, but then again, nothing is. Are they non-incremental and exciting enough to get funded? Perhaps. It depends on the panel and how good a job I end up doing with the writing. I will have been mulling over the ideas in the back of my mind for months, and then it's time to start writing what the folks who apply to the National Institutes of Health would call "specific aims" and the NSF folks call "themes," "topics," "thrusts," or (rarely) "aims"; sometimes people call them "tasks" or "goals" or "objectives." Bottom line is − if you can articulate three to five main lines of study, each worth two or three papers, those are your proposal information quanta. Partition your narrative any finer, and you risk being told that you are presenting "a laundry list of topics" or that you are "going on a fishing expedition" or that "the proposal lacks focus" (all panel favorites).

Sometimes, I am not burning with desire to work on the topics on which I will write. There are other things I would love to do more, but I either can't get the money for them (now or ever, here in the US at least) or I am too much of a novice to the relevant subfields to be able to write a competitive proposal at this time. The need to write proposals, coupled with a perpetual lack of time to learn new things, ends up resulting in (at least me) not being as mobile between subfields as I would like. I know, I know, that's the system and it's not going away, but I can at least indulge myself with a little exasperated whine-and-rant combo before it's time to roll up my sleeves again and get crackin'. Those proposals aren't gonna write themselves.

Chapter 6

Working with Grad Students and Postdocs

Are You Your Advisor?

One of the many similarities between advising and parenting is that the harshest critics are those people who have never been parents themselves. Many of us who have kids thought we'd do everything so much better once it was our turn, only to find out that things are so much harder than we anticipated and that other people's parenting choices, which we so vehemently criticized, start to completely make sense once we've had kids. It's the same with advising junior scientists — everything looks much different once you actually have to do it yourself.

Much of what we do, as advisors, is affected by how we were advised. Sometimes, the things that made us furious when we were trainees make a lot of sense once we are on the other side. Yes, just like how you develop newfound appreciation for your own parents after you become a parent yourself. Then there are the undeniable differences with respect to our advisors, simply because we are indeed different people; we may be at drastically different stages in our careers, at different types of institutions, have different personalities, or simply envision a different work–life balance for ourselves and our group members. Here are a few vignettes from my grad-school life, which I think influenced how I advise students now.

1) I got a faculty position right after grad school, so my PhD advisor is the advisor who had the greatest influence on my career. (For others, a postdoc advisor might have been dominant.) My advisor was very well known and awe inspiring. He also had a reputation for having a really bad temper and being extremely bellicose with colleagues, which hurt his recognition and did not help his advisees, either. He did not like being wrong or challenged in an environment where he perceived he would lose face; you could see his blood boiling and him becoming increasingly agitated and unpleasant when it appeared that he was losing an argument. I learned that the best way to handle this was to drop the issue that we argued about and let him cool down, and then follow up with an email. He was, at the end of the day, always in pursuit of the truth and would eventually acknowledge when I was right; the key was to finalize the exchange after everyone had the time to process it. I think this workaround to counter his temper was key to the two of us getting along very well, much better than he got along with many other students. It is also important that, every single time, the original idea was always much improved after having talked or emailed with him. Even when he wasn't right, the process of hashing it all out was extremely stimulating and useful.

What's the moral of this story? One is that advisors are people, with all that entails. They are not infallible or stoic; they get tired and pissed and defensive, and everything else that other people get, so consider this aspect in your interactions. Second, when I have a disagreement with a student or postdoc, this experience has taught me not to get defensive or aggressive (I am not 100 percent successful in this aspect, I admit) but to persevere in the discussion for everyone's benefit. Even when you, the advisor, are wrong, you typically have a lot to bring to the discussion, because you have much more experience in various aspects of the scientific process, so the idea is always much better and cleaner after the interaction than before it.

2) My advisor had a number of nonnegotiable rules. For instance, I was trying for years to convince him to use LaTeX for text processing, and he would never budge. It was MS Word exclusively for all text, PowerPoint for all presentations, and one specific programming language and one image processing software. Nobody was allowed to use anything else for anything research related. At the time, I honestly thought he was just a petty tyrant. Now I know the benefit of uniformity for streamlining everything in the group, from training new members to software license renewal, debugging and troubleshooting, and sharing code and other files.

This story teaches us a couple of things, too. One is that, while you work in someone's group, it's going to be their way, whether you like it or not. Once you are on your own and lead your own group, you can do things any way you like. Another point is that some rules are there for a good reason, which may not be obvious until you are in your advisor's shoes. Try to give them the benefit of the doubt that they actually may know what they are doing.

3) My advisor was very hands off in other aspects of mentoring students. We had intermittent group meetings; he would rarely seek a student out and would generally expect you to come to see him if you had problems. If you asked to see him, though, he'd accommodate you pretty promptly, usually the same day, even though he was very busy. I was happy with this style and I think it works well for people who are independent. But I knew there were group members who would do nothing for weeks or would go off on unproductive tangents for far too long. Once they got

together with the advisor after a long time and presented what was clearly suboptimal output, unbelievable wrath was unleashed upon them. This reaction only made them even less likely to seek meetings in the future and the vicious cycle continued. In my own group, we have weekly group meetings as well as weekly individual meetings. My best students would likely be fine left alone for longer, but for most students, especially when they are novices, weekly one-on-one meetings keep them out of trouble and away from being stuck for long, and the feedback offers them reassurance that they are doing well.

What's the moral of this story? Don't assume independence in all your students. Actually, assume that most will not be as driven or as independent as you might like them to be, at least initially, and ensure they have enough structure to maximize their own potential and make progress in good time. This is critical, especially in the initial stages of a research project. Brilliant students do well almost irrespective of advisor. I think a successful advisor is one who can get decent-quality research output from a student who is not entirely independent or obviously brilliant from the start — for many such students, picking out a good topic and seeing them through their initial struggles can actually reveal a great hidden potential as they gain some confidence. Structure and regular feedback are key in this scenario.

4) When I was a grad student I was quite productive, wrote many papers, and went to many conferences. My advisor even threw several of his invited talks my way. I traveled more than his average student, attending probably five or six conferences per year in my last few years. When I became faculty, I thought that's what I needed to do — send my students to as many conferences as possible and have them present all the work.

But there was one significant difference between my advisor and me. When I was a graduate student, he was in his 60s, well known and well funded. He needed neither exposure nor funding, and could send me wherever, whenever. I, on the other hand, was a newbie faculty — I neither had his funding resources nor the name recognition and clout that he commanded. I had to balance sending students to conferences against ensuring that I myself got enough exposure, and do it all on what were initially relatively modest funds. I only realized this after several senior faculty colleagues kept insisting that I myself needed to travel and get seen in order to get tenure, and that delegating everything to students at the beginning of my career would be devastating. So my students initially went to two, occasionally three conferences per year. I also did not start delegating my invited talks (which were initially quite few and far between) to group members until I was near the end of my tenure track; invited talks mean a lot on the CV in my discipline and count for a lot at tenure-review time. Was this selfish? Perhaps. But had I not received tenure, I would not have ended up being of much use to anyone, including my students in their subsequent careers.

5) As a graduate student, I substituted for my advisor in the classroom a lot. *A lot.* One semester, I actually ended up teaching more classes than him even though I was not the official TA or anything like that. He would just tell me that he was going out of town for two weeks and that I needed to cover certain chapters from the book in class. I don't know why he did it — initially it looked like he would distribute the subbing load among his students, but at some point it became only me. My guess is that he knew I wanted to be faculty and figured I could use some practice. I think I ended up substituting for him in about five different courses during my grad school career. I actually enjoyed it, but it

often required a lot of time to prepare and it did take away from my research projects.

While I also give my students teaching opportunities, I ask them first if anyone wants to substitute. For some of them, it would be a good idea, considering that they either want to teach or simply need practice talking in front of an audience, in which case I try to nudge them to do it and explain my reasons for thinking they should. But, if nobody wants to, which is usually the case, I don't make them do it. I consider teaching classes to be my obligation; the learning outcomes of the class, especially with undergrads, do depend strongly on the quality of teaching, and if I have to twist arms to get someone to cover a lecture, the lecture is not going to be a fun experience for anyone. Instead, I schedule a make-up class.

STUDENTS DIG THE
PAULI EXCLUSION PRINCIPLE

Beyond Scores

M_y department is ranked in the top-15 research programs in my field; it's quite a good place, but we don't routinely bring in superstar student candidates. However, I believe that if we are a bit clever in how we recruit, we can find some true gems among the students who get passed up by more highly ranked schools because there is something a bit off with their record.

In the physical sciences, American students have multiple fellowship opportunities available to them and are therefore (on average) easier to fund than international students. This is part of the reason why good American students are very attractive to hire and they routinely get snatched up by places more highly ranked than mine. So, in order to find some good talent willing to come here, I typically look hard at international student applications. I give a lot of weight to the quality of the undergrad institution, grades in math and physics, letters of recommendation, research experience and papers (if the student has any), as well as my previous experiences with students from the same school. As for tests, I look at TOEFL scores for international students and GRE Quantitative Reasoning, but not at Verbal or Analytic. Unfortunately, there are several countries that produce students who have very high Verbal scores, but when they come to the US it turns out they don't speak English fluently at all and have trouble following classes. The Analytic part, since they changed it to "Analytical Writing" is, in my opinion, completely useless for selection in my field. These are essays scored by humans; being able to persuasively write in college-essay format in English is not a skill most international students have when they take the GRE test, even if they speak the language well and have decent listening comprehension. The average quality of English instruction and the availability of resources for test preparation vary greatly from nation to nation and this should be taken into account when looking at test scores. Also, in many countries, the GRE and TOEFL tests aren't offered very often, might still be paper-based, and taking the tests more than once may be prohibitively costly for the student.

One year I was going to bring in another student from a university from which I had previously recruited good students; even spectacular students from that country tend to do so-so on the GRE. The new candidate had excellent math and physics grades and stellar letters of recommendation, and had even published a paper in a reputable journal. The student also had a maximal GRE General Test quantitative score and a very good score on a GRE Subject Test relevant to what I do. We had been in contact and I was sure he would get formally admitted without a problem.

Then the student contacted me, very upset, saying he was rejected. I was stunned. I inquired around a bit with our admissions committee, and apparently the person who looked at the student's file thought his GRE Analytical Writing score of three was too low and that was what got the student nixed. For comparison, my two excellent American-born and -educated undergrad researchers, who both went on to top-five places for their PhDs, received fours on their GRE General Analytical Writing; I think holding international students to the same standard is pretty ridiculous. The colleague who examined the student's file appeared defensive about the decision, which leads me to believe he hadn't even analyzed the rest of the student's file carefully.

I had to make a stink about it (thankfully, tenure enables me to do this) and the student's file was reconsidered. But this leaves a bad taste — that a good student can be dismissed based on a pretty irrelevant test score. I know people on admissions committees work hard, there are a number of applications to go through, and it's very time consuming as far as service roles go. Picking cutoffs to streamline the process seems like a must. But I feel we admit too many poorly prepared or insufficiently motivated candidates, but, most importantly, too many candidates who don't have the background for the type of research that the faculty in this department do.

Having high and inflexible selection criteria may seem to convey that we are a top-notch, hard-core place. We are, in the sense that there is very good science being done here, but let's not kid ourselves. We are not a magnet school, so we do not have our pick among the cream of the crop. We have to be smarter than inflexible admissions and test scores. We need to be more efficient at identifying and attracting the not-so-obviously superb students who will be interested in coming here. As my recent experience demonstrates, this is surprisingly hard to implement, especially at a level higher than a research group (i.e., department, college, university), where the different stages of the admissions process are decoupled from one another.

Switch-a-roo

A professor's first graduated PhD student remains forever special. Mine is now happily employed by a national lab, has a family, and is doing great. It is always a great pleasure to see her.

I met her in my first semester on the tenure track. I was a typical overzealous, overly demanding newbie teacher who wanted to cover way too much material; many students were struggling. She had no background in my area and was taking the course to satisfy a breadth requirement, yet she was catching on extremely quickly, and by the end of the course left everyone in the dust pretty spectacularly. I was quite impressed, and would have loved to have her join my group, but she had already been working with another professor for a few years.

The semester ended, a few months passed, and she found me to ask if she could switch to my group, because she was unhappy where she was. I can't remember the details why; I think the project was ill defined or otherwise unappealing. I was thrilled to have her join my group, but at the same time I was absolutely terrified — I was untenured. What if her advisor decided to somehow retaliate? I talked with my chair and my faculty mentors to make sure they knew I hadn't poached her, that she came to me on her own. I never talked to her former advisor, partly because I had never met him (he's an affiliate of the department), and partly because I was clueless about proper etiquette and very scared.

She was the first student who switched to my group. By the end of the year, I had three more who switched — one came from my alma mater with an MS, two from other advisors in my department. By then I knew better; each time a student wanted to switch to my group, if I thought it was a good idea, I requested they go talk to the soon-to-be-former advisor first and I followed up in person to make sure everyone was on board and happy.

Over the years, I have had several students switch to my group. The vast majority of them worked out really well and the switch was a good idea for everyone involved. In several cases, the former advisor actually encouraged the switch because it was clear that the skills and inclinations of the student were simply not a good fit for that group, but the student was generally smart and motivated.

I have also lost students to other groups; one wanted to upgrade schools, and two left with an MS and joined another group in which the style of work and the topics addressed were considerably different. I remember being furious when I had to let the first student go after two years of paying him as an RA; there was no doubt in my mind that he could not stay in my group, but I lamented all the money spent (of which I didn't have much at that point).

But, after a bit of experience, it becomes clear that students switching groups is simply a fact of life. Actually, a student switching groups once is a fairly common occurrence in the physical-science fields, because there are no rotations (a practice in the biomedical sciences) that the students can use to test the waters in different groups before committing. My attitude is that you win some, you lose some: as long as you are not exclusively hemorrhaging students or actively poaching other people's advisees, it's a wash.

To the graduate students who are unhappy, but terrified about switching groups: in my experience, professors don't generally think it's a sign of your deficiency if you want to switch groups. If your former advisor is a sane and decent person, they will let the new advisor know about your strengths and weaknesses, about how you got along, and why things didn't work out. If you have really tried to make it work in your current group, but it just isn't happening, it is OK to consider changing. But do think really hard about where you want to land, because you don't want to do it a second time if you can help it.

Postdocs Only

On a recent NSF panel, an interesting issue came up: a PI wanted to spend all of the generally modest amount of money on a postdoc plus some summer salary. The proposal was not competitive, but the budget description led to some interesting discussions among panelists. My understanding is that education and outreach are large components of the NSF mission. In the particular directorate where this review was happening, postdocs are really not the norm at all. People overwhelmingly ask for money for grad students, or occasionally a grad student and a partial postdoc; I had never before seen a grant proposal in which the PI has no intention of supporting any students at all.

As this issue was raised and a few panelists chimed in, the proposal's champion basically went on to tell us how the PI's background is such that "They (people with that same background) don't like to work with graduates students, just with postdocs, because students aren't good enough."

Let's leave aside the obnoxious implication that the work of some people is very hard and important, in contrast to the pedestrian and irrelevant efforts that the rest of us engage in. But where do all these brilliant postdocs come from? Someone had to train them. Someone had to actually want to work with the student and then coach them for years in doing, writing, and presenting science, getting them from a terrified novice to the level of competence for which we grant PhD degrees. Many people doing very complicated science train graduate students, with or without the help of postdocs, so the issue is not how complex the work is at all. In my own work, I will take a third- or fourth-year graduate student whom I have trained over an average postdoc from another group any day. The PI who can supposedly only work with postdocs is a leech on the community, benefiting from the training that others have invested into creating scientists, without giving back by training someone themselves.

Musings on Postdoc-ing

I have heard several horror stories about the careers of smart young people going to hell after a disastrous postdoc. This reminds me of a particular scenario I sometimes see, either through personal communication or during proposal review, and which always rubs me the wrong way. It goes like this: The PI wants to bring in a postdoc to work on the topics where the PI has neither previous experience nor a collaborator with said experience. Presumably, the postdoc will be brought in from elsewhere to build up the group's expertise in this area. Let's assume you get the world's best postdoc, future superstar, and they are completely independent, they need no supervision whatsoever, just someone to pay the bills and leave them alone to prodigiously do their work. This postdoc would be super productive and publish a lot and teach the advisor's students and the advisor all about the technique. Sounds great, right?

But why would this magical unicorn postdoc go to this group if they are supposed to do exactly what they used to do before? To crank out the maximum number of papers? In that case, they should stay in the PhD advisor's group and get even more done without breaking their stride. Why not go somewhere where they could augment their skill set and become even more awesome?

In my view, postdocs are supposed to enhance both their own portfolio and that of their postdoc advisor, and there should be some overlap between the core expertise of the PI's group and that of the postdoc. If there is only a loosely sketched project that the postdoc is literally supposed to do without help, that is a problem. Chances of this postdoc being successful are slim, unless they can offset the risk by engaging in satellite projects with other people around who could help. Of course, this brings us back to learning from other group members.

Hopefully, the PI is a wonderful advisor who will make sure the group learns from the postdoc while the postdoc also gets to learn from the group, gets a lot of freedom, gains new skills, and tries new research directions. Hopefully, the postdoc is proactive and communicative and manages to get help from his or her former group or independently establishes new collaborations.

Maybe I am just cranky because I have heard way too many horror stories recently about the careers of smart young people going to hell after a disastrous postdoc, but I wish some PIs would take better care of the people over whose careers they have so much sway.

Murphy's Law of Graduate-Student Recruitment

When you have grant money, there are no good students around, so you end up hiring whoever's available and often waste said money. When there are good students to recruit, as a rule you have no money to pay them.

What's a professor to do? Here's the advice given to me by a successful senior colleague, who is also a wonderful mentor: When you find someone good, recruit them anyway and the money will work out, somehow. In fact, you will be highly motivated to raise new funds when you know it's to support great people.

Doing Science, Advising Students, and a Bit of Shockley

There is a small assignment I like to give my beginning grad students or upper-level undergrads who want to do research in my group. The assignment is a reasonably simple but quite accurate simulation of a system they all encountered during undergraduate studies. Most students never really ask themselves what approximations are made to produce the textbook results. The simulation, which is perhaps several hundred lines of code, helps the students learn about the numerical techniques, as well as about the theory that describes the behavior of the physical system beyond the textbook approximations.

I have a new undergrad who is great, smart and motivated, and who fits in the group very well. If I am lucky, he will stay here to get his master's and then will likely go someplace with better brand-name recognition to do a PhD. I understand that's what the student must do as it's the reasonable thing to do, but at baseline it's always somewhat infuriating. When some colleagues at Über Unis look down on us State School professors, I wonder whether they ever realize that those awesome kids with research experience who get into their labs did not sprout from the ground; somebody who knows how to do science has actually trained them. The best American students in the physical sciences have plenty of options to attend the most prestigious universities and, if they are well advised (by whom, I wonder?) to realize what's out there for them to apply for, they can do it on prestigious fellowships.

The undergrad did a great job and his code performed the required checks accurately. I said, "Great! Now you can use it to teach us something new about the model system." The student was puzzled and we talked a bit. He came back a week later with what he felt were pretty boring results, not knowing whether there would be anything interesting in such a simple system. I said, "These are all the things off the top of my head that you could inquire: How realistic are all the textbook approximations, to what extent do they hold up in a more realistic simulation, how important are all these different details in the simulation for capturing the right physics, what happens if you completely disregard this or that and how it would translate to reality ..." You get the point. He thought there was nothing there and to me there were 15 interesting things to ask. I gave him my little speech about how code is like a piece of experimental equipment — once you are done lovingly building it, the science part is deciding what questions are both worth asking and are possible to answer with the tool that you have.

This exchange reminded me of a famous paper by William Shockley, "On the Statistics of Individual Variations of Productivity in Research Laboratories."[1] Shockley was a Nobel Prize winner (with John Bardeen and Walter Brattain) for the invention of the transistor, and was believed by many to be one of the most brilliant and most nasty people they had ever met. (Shockley was said to have had "reverse charisma" — when he entered the room, you'd instantly dislike him.) Shockley had been able to identify and recruit smart people for Shockley Semiconductor Labs, whom he then drove away ("The Traitorous Eight") into Fairchild Semiconductor, a company that became the incubator for Silicon Valley, having spun off a number of companies ("Fairchildren"), such as Intel and AMD.

Shockley's paper is worth reading for a number of reasons. It is actually famous for its discussion of the log-normal distribution of productivity over professional scientists. What I find interesting here is Shockley's hypothesis that productivity depends on the ability to clear eight different hurdles. *Being good at all of them is key;* you cannot be exceptional at one thing and inadequate at

---

[1] Proceedings of the IRE 45, 279 (1957), doi: 10.1109/JRPROC.1957.278364

another, as success depends on the product of functions that measure one's:

1. Ability to think of a good problem

2. Ability to work on it

3. Ability to recognize a worthwhile result

4. Ability to make a decision as to when to stop and write up the results

5. Ability to write adequately

6. Ability to profit constructively from criticism

7. Determination to submit the paper to a journal

8. Persistence in making changes (if necessary as a result of journal action)

Everything here depends in part on talent, personality, and training, much of the latter by osmosis.

For instance, there are many students who have #2, i.e., they are smart enough to work on a good problem, provided that someone else formulates it (#1). It takes talent as well as experience to learn what constitutes a good problem, the right combination of interesting and doable in a reasonable time and with available resources. It's similar with #3 and #4 — it takes experience to know when something has become a publishable nugget, when the data is enough to support a compelling and convincing insight. Once you realize that #5 and #7 are important (and they really, really are — all the nice work you might have done is as good as nonexistent until you publish it), you need to have a good PhD or postdoc advisor from whom you can learn how to write well. If you are a talented person, you can become really good at many of these aspects early in your career with good, focused training. Otherwise, it can take you much longer to realize the importance and then teach yourself the skills, and your early career can be impeded.

Numbers 6 and 8 essentially mean grit and are extremely important, probably even more important for grants than papers these days. Most of my grad students get discouraged when we get "revise and resubmit" with potentially lengthy revisions, because they feel we had already submitted a great product, so why all this silliness now? And they may or may not have a point, but the key is to go on. I have had to do it many times already, and I am simply desensitized to it. We have to do it, so we do it, but I see that students can wonder whether all the effort is worth it. At the end, the result is a paper. You have to love getting papers published. And having a thick skin does not hurt.

It's fun to think about what success entails and exciting to see a young person start to learn about the moving parts of the enterprise of science — what it means to formulate a problem, execute a project, and finally disseminate new knowledge.

I really love advising students.

The Seven-Year-PhD Itch

Over the course of the past few weeks, the topic of average PhD duration at different institutions came up. I am in the physical sciences; it is normal to expect variations among fields, but in a single field you'd think the PhD should take more or less the same amount of time across different research institutions. In reality, that turns out not to be true.

One colleague tells me that at his (elite) institution, a PhD in the same field as mine lasts six to seven years. At my institution, it's about four to five years. The two-year difference is essentially equivalent to keeping the student on student pay, but working as a postdoc. At the end of their seven-year PhD, these students are better trained than those after five years and have longer, better-looking CVs with lengthy publication lists, which definitely helps with getting academic jobs.

Yet, the prevalent sentiment on the Internet, in the academic blogosphere, is that simply having a student do a PhD in your group is somehow intrinsically exploitative and that the student should be allowed to graduate as soon as possible and go into the mythical "real world." The sentiment is that the PhD training is this unfair, torturous ordeal, which the student has to endure in order to get the diploma and that learning, doing science, writing papers, and giving talks are all dues that the student pays grudgingly in return for a piece of paper. Advisors are for some reason evil to insist on these dues being paid, as if it were somehow possible for a student to receive a PhD without doing the work.

So, how much work is expected to be done for a PhD? I had a double-digit number of journal papers from my PhD, nearly all as first author. I was motivated, I loved doing science, and I had an advisor who was willing and able to give me free rein. I also liked writing papers and I wrote them quickly. I really don't expect my students (a majority of them) to do that, or to even *want* to do that.

Students expect to be treated fairly and equally, but I am not sure they realize these are not synonymous, as they all want different things from their PhDs. One wants to just get out of here and get a job in industry, so I say three papers and you can go. Then another one says he wants to get out with three papers, too; I say, sure, but you also want to be a professor, and with three papers you are not particularly competitive for postdocs. Why don't you stay another year and really cash in on all the nice work you have done so far, really crank some papers out now that everything is working? But he wants to get out because the other guy did, and then when he's not competitive and gets buried in a dead-end postdoc, it's somehow my fault. (The thing with grad students is that they are young and often don't have the needed perspective; ironically, the most talented ones are often the most stubborn ones, who think they know better than the advisor and sometimes end up undermining themselves.)

I understand why people keep a student seven years and not five. You invest so much time in a student and by the time they finally reach some level of competence, they want to leave, and you are back to working with untrained folks all over again. I can completely understand wanting to keep a good person around and actually get some useful work out of them. I understand that it seems selfish from the standpoint of the average student, but it doesn't take a rocket scientist to see that it's good for the enterprise of science to be done by fully trained people and not by people in training; some academically inclined students don't actually seem to mind staying a little longer and getting the few extra papers out. One asks why not just pay them postdoc wages? Maybe the advisor is being cheap, but maybe it's the fact that it actually does not look very good to stay at the same place for a postdoc; it looks better on a CV to be a grad student a little longer then go elsewhere for a real postdoc.

If you are in a field like mine, all your students are paid as research assistants on grants the entire time. That's right; graduate school costs money, and federal funds pay for the student to go to school and get training, and in return it is expected that research will be done and scientific papers will be produced. Each student is probably a very poor investment of federal funds in the first two years, but they have to pay the rent and eat the entire time. The student should be very productive in years three to five to actually make the whole investment worthwhile from the standpoint of the funding agencies. I really don't understand the people who say it's swell to have your school and stipend paid for, and then also have the gall to insist on graduating without papers.

Doing academic science, while being to a great degree about training (how much exactly depends on the funding agency), is really *not primarily* about training. It's about doing science professionally, with a mixture of trainees and career scientists. Funding is there to do the science, it's not a gift or a handout or a guarantee for anyone. In many fields, such as the humanities, people would be extremely grateful to be paid to do the research on their dissertation. Publishing research papers in return is far from a horrible thing to require.

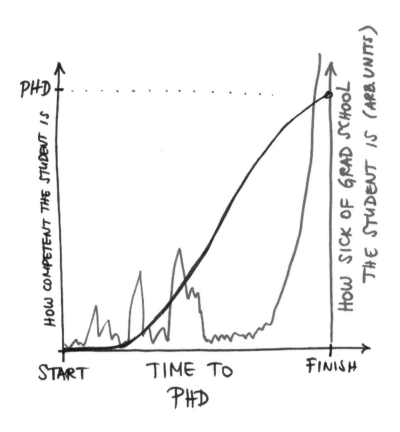

Potential and Ambition

It can be very frustrating to come across a very talented student, with great potential in your area of study, but who has no interest in applying themselves toward achieving excellence. When you are someone who works in a field that has always been your passion, it is indeed quite disheartening to see a person who has what it takes to succeed, but who simply does not care.

It took me a while on the tenure track to accept that most students didn't share my ambition. They just want to get a well-paying job, no matter how much potential for this or that they might have. Some students simply aren't interested in doing research for a living, irrespective of how good they could be at it. Research doesn't float their boat. I am not sure what else does; perhaps nothing at all. There are, in fact, a great many people who go through their lives without developing an overwhelming passion for any activity. This is a hard truth for overachievers to fathom.

Last semester I taught an undergraduate class. There were several students in there who I thought would do splendidly in grad school. I spoke with a couple of the best, and neither wanted to go to grad school. One was a laid-back kid, who reminded me of my eldest offspring; this student shared that he was paired up with a very intense young woman and was very happy to just go with the flow and follow her. Another felt very strongly that he had to get a job and start earning money right out of college, and he will do great wherever he lands. Of this cohort, the most intense kid, one with passion and focus, was an AB student; very good indeed, but not the absolute best technically. He really knew what he wanted to do and was voracious about learning more.

We could lament the fact that the best students wouldn't become career scientists, but so what? They are smart kids; they can do whatever they want with their lives. Besides, what does "the best" even mean? Potential and talent are very nebulous; they just mean you could do well in a certain broad field, but if you don't actually apply yourself, talent doesn't mean very much. However, a student who is very good and very focused can indeed get far, potentially as far as their passion carries them.

In the US, there is a prevalent singular-focus mindset. You have only one talent, only one outstanding thing about you, and you have to embrace it, have it define you, and hone the related skill with all your might, potentially at the expense of everything else. This mindset, which is quite foreign to most of Europe, is why there are also so many achievement-related stereotypes in the US. The dumb athlete is one — of course you can only be athletically blessed; you could not possibly have other ambitions or talents, because being able to throw a football somehow precludes being able to do math, sing, or paint. Then there is the stereotype of the socially clueless, athletically hopeless geek, as if one could not possibly be able to understand calculus, swim fast, and have a girlfriend. Based on my experience, most smart kids have multiple talents; there are several things they could do quite well, even if not prodigiously. For instance, I know a number of kids who can write very well, sing, play an instrument, play a sport, and also excel academically. Who's to say which one of these avenues the kid should pursue? Some are very passionate about one of the things they can do, but many are lukewarm about all of them. In fact, based on a lot of time spent around geeks, and having taught at a high school for the gifted in math and the physical sciences, I would say that most kids don't have strong passions early on. I am sure someone somewhere has done research on this topic, but my gut feeling is that the following happens: When you have a very smart kid, things come easily to them, and everything being easy may be an obstacle to developing a keen interest in anything. To develop a passion for something there needs to be an equal mixture of awe and challenge.

Having been a professor and a professional scientist for a number of years, I can safely say that there are many more kids with the potential to do science than there are those who actually elect to be scientists or even purse any career with a strong science component. Many of these kids have other talents and interests that they may prefer to focus on. Some have a number of abilities and they never really decide what it is that they are pursing, but are rather satisfied just dabbling. What we "type A" professors have to realize is that we are talking about these kids' lives, which they are completely entitled to spend however they like, even if it means not using their potential in science or any other potential at all. To us, it may seem like a waste, but to someone who never thought of science as cool or enticing, just something they can easily do if they have to, it probably doesn't seem like a waste at all. Being free to make choices means you are free to excel at whatever you want or not excel at anything.

Maybe the people who are not tightly wound overachievers have a point. One day, we'll all be dead and most of us will prove to be completely inconsequential in every way imaginable, except for perhaps having left a little bit of DNA. Instead of focusing on achievement, which for most of us appears to be just smoke and mirrors, why not enjoy the people around us, the connections for which we are apparently wired, the sunsets and good books and the giggles of our kids and grandkids? I can answer for the likes of me: because there is an internal engine that does not allow us to sit idle and just take in the world and the people we love; because this awesomeness does not scratch the perennial brain itch. But we should also learn to live and let live, and find ways to work productively with our smart and happy but itchless students, and not consider their lack of ambition to be anybody's failure.

Advice on Job Hunting for a Recent PhD Graduate

Reader E recently completed their PhD in a physical-science field at a top university. The first three years were spent on experimental work, while E was supported by a fellowship. By the end of the fellowship, external funds for the continuation of the project did not come through. In the meantime, E's advisor took a part-time position elsewhere and had been largely unavailable to E. At the end of the fellowship, E was advised to leave due to the lack of funding. Then it was decided E would switch gears and do a computational project. So, E spent the last two-and-a-half years learning how to do computational work with the help of another senior person, because E's advisor did not have the needed expertise.

While E completed the computational project successfully and has recently defended their PhD, they don't feel like the PhD experience has made them competitive for jobs:

"While I produced several articles (2 journals, 1 proceeding), I wouldn't call any of them career producing (the best was a mid-range journal) … I feel like I learned how to apply a very narrow set of computational skills to an even narrower problem. I have a hard time showing employers (postdoc, industry, gov, etc … not picky at all at this stage … have a growing family and need a job) that my skill set would be beneficial to them. My advisor has no way of helping me get employed (knows no one in the computational field …) and my mentor [the person who helped E get started on the computational front] is too busy with new professional developments. I would like to know, do you offer students (without a network to rely on) and struggling to get employed

how to sell themselves? I would love to stay in science, but accept the fact that it is very unlikely that someone will take a chance on me."

This is what I tell my students, early and often: This is not MIT or the like, and I am not famous. Just getting a PhD from here, with me as advisor, does not magically open doors. I tell them that I am very good at what I do and we will do good science together, that they will be well trained to be good PhD scientists and communicators, technically strong, who can write and present their work. But, I tell them that I also really want them to be able to get jobs when they are done. So they are encouraged from the beginning to get an MS in another field of their choice in addition to the PhD, and to take classes in other areas. I seem to be unusual in this respect, as I recently found out — most of my colleagues seem worried about productivity and want their students focused on research 100 percent of the time. I don't. After the first couple of years, the students are done with classes for the major, and the resulting lack of class-induced structure to their days and weeks can be disorienting. I strongly encourage them to take one and sometimes two classes per semester in whatever they want until they are done; not only does this increase their knowledge base and potential employability, but I strongly believe it helps productivity on their main projects. (Alternatively, they TA when they are senior; regular contact with chirpy undergrads is good for the grumpy senior grad student.) Nearly all of my students have taken the opportunity to get an MS in another STEM field while doing a PhD in our field (and they get a "master's in passing" in the major, but that's just a bit of trivial paperwork for a well-performing student en route to a PhD).

I also have some connections in industry (e.g., my grad-school buddies). Now that some of my former students have also joined the ranks of corporate America, they could (and do) further help other group members. From my standpoint, all I can do is help as much as I can with the connections I have, let the students know early on what the lay of the land is, and then leave them to figure it out for themselves. I am about to graduate a student who has a job lined up at a major software company. It has been a great experience: he interviewed, they gave him an offer, he asked and they agreed on a start date several months into the future, so he will both finish his project and his dissertation without a rush, and will then start at his great new job.

My industry-bound students seem to do a few interviews to get a job, but not many; between one and three is the norm before first offer. Only one former student, several years ago, had about a dozen interviews before the first offer, and eventually landed at a company that he had always dreamed of working for (I helped there by forcing him to go give a talk or two at the venues where I knew the company would have representatives). It has never been an issue that my students can't get interviews.

I think it's impossible to get a job without some sort of network, but it needn't be your advisor and his buddies. Former group members are great, compatriots are great, and checking websites of companies in the area or the companies you'd like to work with in general is great. In my experience, while the job search is scary, it has always ended very well for my students and it didn't take long. As an advisor, I know that the last six months of the student's time here will be low productivity, because they are distracted and interviewing, and that's fine; I plan on everything being done beforehand anyway.

Postdoc experiences could range from awesome, which will propel you, to awful, which will kill years of your life and, in some fields, might even make you less employable in industry.

The worst part is that you don't know that postdoc opportunities are available until they are (i.e., the notice of funding comes through) and then they are filled quickly and usually through personal connections (e.g., I will prioritize a student from a group whose leader I know and respect over a random other applicant).

When it comes to advising, it seems to me that people with fellowships, especially graduate students, but sometimes also postdocs, tend to have a crappy time disproportionately often. Unfortunately, I am guessing it's the case of "Well, I don't have to pay the kid, so why not?" My rule is that if I wouldn't work with a student/postdoc under the assumption that I am paying them off my grants, then I don't take them (this doesn't imply poor quality of student or postdoc, but rather that they may be a poor fit for the group, or that I already have too many people and cannot effectively mentor another one). The same holds for the research topic: too often, people on fellowships end up working on the advisor's pet topic that may or may not be half-baked; they also end up being poorly supervised, because there is no funding-agency pressure that the advisor feels for regular grants. Obviously, that's a recipe for disaster: before you know it, three years have passed, and the student has spent them on a poorly defined project with inadequate advising. Likely, it doesn't help that most fellowship holders flock to tippity-top schools, which are competitive places and not known to be oases of warmth or fuzziness in student advising.

So, what's the moral of the story and advice for reader E?

The good news is that a PhD from a fancy school won't hurt in the long run. Right now, pull all the strings you can — whomever you know, whomever they know, look at online postings, anything you can find. You don't necessarily expect people to get

165

you jobs, but rather to help point you toward jobs or the places where jobs might be opening. It's never too late to develop a network, and a network can be built in ways that you don't expect, e.g., there are lawyers and doctors and professors and entrepreneurs among the parents on my kid's swim team; sure, I know them because of swimming, but I know them now, and didn't before, and if need be I could and would call upon our acquaintance in another context, and I would be happy if they did the same. Just meet people, and opportunities will arise.

There Are Humans in Academia

In the academic blogosphere, we often discuss how we, as advisors, need to be understanding and permissive of graduate students. But I think communication might further be improved if the junior people extended similar courtesy to the senior folks. While students and postdocs expect to have their own work–life balance respected and accommodated, they don't seem to view advisors as fully human, with strengths and limitations; they don't ask themselves how their advisor lives, what motivates or propels him or her. I do know it's hard for junior people to completely put themselves in a senior person's shoes, largely because it's hard to empathize when you haven't actually had many of the older person's experiences.

I often mention this example from graduate school, where I was able to communicate very well with my notoriously difficult advisor upon realizing what made him angry (losing face), avoiding triggers, and discussing tough topics via email. I have friends from grad school for whom our advisor is still a mysterious beast, as opposed to a senior person with his own hang-ups, regrets, insecurities, and career path, but also someone who can be their big professional champion.

I wonder how much of it is socialization across gender lines. The men I know well seem to spend vanishingly little time thinking about what anyone else is thinking or feeling; they don't want to hurt anyone, but they go merrily on their way, doing what they want, until someone complains. I see it in my male colleagues, too, even very junior ones. I was a complete ball of nerves and insecurity when I was a junior professor, nearly paralyzed by a combination of the fear that I would mess things up because I didn't know what I was doing and the fear that I would be inconveniencing people by asking them for advice. My junior male colleagues are much more bold (even when they objectively ought to ask for advice) and much more unapologetic about requesting help (or anything else they need). They are laser-focused on what they need and want, and perhaps only in the rear-view mirror they occasionally glance at the effect they might have left behind. In contrast, many female colleagues and I spend enormous amounts of energy wondering whether we are entitled to do what we want or need, and who might be inconvenienced or upset by our actions. I bet this energy drain is a major cause of burnout.

I just had a master's-degree student, after I had signed off on the paperwork, simply declare in a group meeting that they didn't want to fulfill what we had agreed they would do before the end of the semester (generate certain plots so we could write a short paper) because they were "busy with classes." My husband says he doesn't think the student is a bad person but that they don't understand that they have violated our agreement; they are probably just happy they get to finish their degree. The thing is, if the student tried not to think about the master's being 100 percent about their own experience and me just being there in the service of it and tried to put themselves in my shoes for a microsecond, they would have realized that the whole thing was not worth my time at all unless they completed what we had agreed on. And I certainly don't like being made a fool of.

I suppose one reason for me writing these essays that have to do with student–advisor interactions is to try to get some junior researchers to view their advisors as people. I know there are bad advisors and generally bad bosses around, and nobody should tolerate being disrespected or abused in any way. This is not about bad advisors. I really think that most advisors are normal people, which means they are human, and as such they are neither omniscient nor clueless, neither omnipotent nor helpless, neither 100 percent selfless nor 100 percent selfish.

Being human, professors have limitations on time and energy, and do not exist for the sole devotion to the betterment of a student's educational experience. PhD and postdoc advisors are people who have their own career interests (which overlap to a great extent, but not 100 percent, with those of the student) as well as their own personality traits and private lives. For everyone's benefit, we should keep it professional, but should also try to have empathy — and it goes both ways.

In a group like mine, most students (being young, unencumbered, and male) have no frame of reference for the life that I lead and the constraints it puts on how the group operates. I wonder if they all leave thinking that they spent years working with a complete alien.

Chapter 7

Technical Writing with Junior Scientists

Summertime, Academic Rendition

Summertime
And the living is easy
Academics
Clean up their manuscripts

Those with students
Pull out their hair, swearing
At sloppy intros
Forgotten writing tips

Use spellchecker
Correct your goddamn references
Oh, my student
Your paper red ink drips

(With apologies to DuBose Heyward and George Gershwin)

Favorite Papers

Among my own papers, some of my favorites are those that I have written when entering a completely new field. It's really exciting when you are trying to map what people have done, which groups do what, what is considered an established theory versus just a hypothesis, and what types of questions the community is really interested in.

And then you spot a gap in the fabric of knowledge, something that appears pretty important but has somehow been missed. You can only do that because you are an outsider who is trying to understand the field; you stumbled across this missing step in the staircase that everyone who's been in the field longer automatically jumps over, or one that people have tried to fix one way or another without doing it conclusively, so in the end they just left it there, gaping.

You get in there and do the work and seal the gap. I have done that several times already, when moving into a new field, and those are beautiful papers, where you are creative, unburdened by the field's tenets, yet tentative, as you are an outsider. Sort of like being a graduate student all over again! Except that you are not; you are a professional scientist. If my experience is representative, these papers might face a bit of an uphill battle getting published, but once they do get published, they catch people's attention, garner citations, and others start paying attention to you.

Why We Write in STEM

Reporting science in written form is an inherent part of doing science. If you don't publish your work, it's as good as nonexistent.

After a piece of work has been completed, papers need to be written up and submitted for publication as soon as possible. There are several reasons for this practice. First, papers are how funding bodies judge the success of a project. Grants have milestones and reviews and renewals, which all need to be respected. Second, the PIs on grants are obligated to the funding agencies and the taxpayers to disseminate the knowledge promptly, so that others can benefit from it and build on it. Writing is to science what eating fiber is to a diet: necessary to keep things moving. Third, for junior PIs, there is the relentless ticking of the tenure-track clock, so publications need to go out fast, or the PI's career will be over.

Teaching students and postdocs how to write technical papers is an important part of PhD and postdoctoral training. Regardless of what they end up doing, they are PhD-holding scientists and engineers, and will be writing technical documents one way or another throughout their careers. Writing is paramount. Therefore, I am all for giving the student or postdoc who did the work the opportunity to draft and revise their manuscript, incorporating detailed comments made by the advisor. However, the junior researcher has to take this task seriously and the text has to significantly improve between drafts; the manuscript actually has to converge to a publishable form within a reasonable time frame, otherwise the student or postdoc loses the privilege (some would say the burden) of working on the text.

Now, what is a "reasonable time frame"? The answer depends on a number of variables. A few that come to mind are:

- Is there a grant application or renewal deadline? Or is it a paper on the work from a grant that ended and won't be renewed?
- Is the PI going up for tenure in the next couple of years?
- Are you in danger of getting scooped?
- Is the publication of this work holding up something else, perhaps more high impact, in the pipeline? (E.g., do you need to get the instrumentation paper published so you can write up a paper on the exciting new experimental finding using said instrumentation?)

Depending on the answers, a paper may need to get out in a matter of weeks, but you may also have months. While on the tenure track, I was considerably more high strung and anxious about papers getting out as soon as possible, and was quicker than I am now to say, "That's enough. I am taking over and rewriting this whole damn thing."

Among professional scientists and engineers, there are some who naturally have more talent for writing than others, yet all have to learn to write competently. Fortunately, technical writing is largely formulaic, so the natural-ability threshold for becoming decent at it is not high. I am confident that any methodical scientist or engineer can become at least a competent writer, regardless of literary talent. But the key is to accept that technical writing is an inherent part of the profession, and that mastering it is not a nuisance.

Who Teaches a Grad Student How to Write?

No junior researcher starts their technical-writing journey by producing flawless prose. Everyone needs guidance early on. Many PIs provide copious comments on the printouts of manuscript drafts, which the student is supposed to take to heart and not only incorporate the corrections in the text, but also learn from and extrapolate for the future, understanding why certain things fly and others don't. Obviously, when things are unclear, the advisor should be available for clarification.

In my experience, there are four types of students based on what happens after that first draft of the first paper.

1) There are the students whose quality of writing ramps up remarkably fast. I don't think that implies these students want to be professors; several of my students who were like that had always wanted to go into industry upon graduation. I also don't think it necessarily correlates with natural writing or speaking ability. Some people really take ownership of their writing proficiency and are very focused on improving it. My first student showed remarkable improvement within the time span of two papers. The first draft of the second manuscript was already in excellent shape: it looked like a scientific article rather than the ruminations of a near-layperson. I have had the fortune of working with several other junior researchers who were similar. These people really strove to improve, analyzed what needed to be changed, were not afraid to seek input from me or others, and were open to criticism.

2) Some students are really not motivated to improve their writing because of a misguided idea that it's unimportant for their

175

jobs in the "real world," only something they need to suffer through in order to get a PhD diploma. No matter how often I tell my students that, regardless of where they work, chances are they will have to write technical texts all the time, some keep thinking they know better and don't want to put in much effort. I had such a student; he published prolifically, but even his very last paper was barely passable after many draft iterations and you could see that he didn't care very much about any of it. He dutifully entered all specific corrections, but refused to engage his brain in writing. I always ended up having to thoroughly rewrite his final drafts even after many, many back-and-forth revisions.

3) Some people think you, the advisor, have stupid and unreasonable demands (such as that the text actually be readable by humans). They think you are ruining their manuscript by dumbing it down, and that the worthy will understand the innumerable "implied" assumptions while the others are unworthy of an explanation anyway. I had a brilliant student who was like that and we would argue over every change. He behaved similarly in regard to comments on his presentations — whenever I said something was unclear and should be presented differently, he would not take it at face value and go fix it, but would instead insist that it is, in fact, clear (and by extension the audience is stupid for not getting it). Needless to say, the student's attitude was the problem, and this problem is unfortunately one that is almost impossible to cure.

4) Many students have the right attitude and are willing to make improvements, but have a hard time deciphering what it is that makes a difference between a well-written manuscript and a poorly written one. There is no substitute here for the advisor pinpointing what the building blocks of a manuscript are, what the students are to look for, and how certain parts are structured,

and providing examples of good and bad writing. I do this with students individually as well as periodically in group meetings. We talk about the common parts of short communications and comprehensive articles, how each part is structured, etc. The abstract and introduction are the hardest for students to write well, and we discuss them thoroughly and often. There are also differences in how to write for *Reputable Society Journal* versus *Prestigious Society Letters* versus *Glamour Magazine*. Discussing these issues with group members is important.

It's tempting to send students to take technical writing courses, but I would advise caution. Recently, a student working with another professor in a three-faculty collaboration submitted the first draft of his manuscript. It was a passive-voice monstrosity. When all three professors gasped, "What's with all the passive voice?!" the student told us that he had taken a technical writing course in which he had been explicitly instructed to only use passive voice for objective facts and first-person singular (plural) when stating his (our) subjective beliefs. Being that this was a technical paper in a physical-science field, the manuscript was almost entirely in passive voice. I have no idea who taught that class, but this is decidedly *not* the way to write scientific articles today; passive voice is used sparingly and there is nothing wrong with saying "We measured ..." or "We concluded ..."

We cannot just send students to be educated by others, without knowing what the students will be getting. Sure, students for whom English is a second language often benefit from writing in a variety of forms, as much as they can. Courses in which the students get feedback on grammar, vocabulary, and general style are likely to be very useful. But when it comes to writing scientific manuscripts, there are conventions that are best taught by practicing scientists. There is no substitute for a motivated student learning from an involved advisor, getting feedback on drafts, then doing their best to understand what the improvements mean and trying to internalize them.

PROFESSORIAL HYPERTENSION

HOW FAST STUDENT IS TO PRODUCE FIRST DRAFT

	SLOW	FAST
ROUGH	BP: 140/90	BP: 110/70
POLISHED	BP: 110/70	CHANCE STUDENT'S A UNICORN: <5% CHANCE PLAGIARISM INVOLVED: >95% BP: 180/110

HOW ROUGH THE DRAFT IS

BP – blood pressure

Write-a-doodle-doo

'Tis that time again — the time for me to write the first paper with a graduate student who is a native English speaker. With the last student who fit this description, every paper was like pulling teeth. While we supposedly discussed the issues behind the friction, it was never plainly spoken that the real reason was the student always thought they knew better than me and refused my edits. This time around, I really hope to nip the issue in the bud before the aggravation gets too bad, as it already seems we might be headed in the same direction.

My native-speaking students invariably start by thinking they are awesome writers and really don't take it kindly when I return corrected drafts. Perhaps they were great at college-level writing, but I find that their first manuscript drafts leave much to be desired, and in a very specific way: the style is conversational, very casual, and the choice of epithets often inappropriate. (Structuring the text is a problem all novice technical writers have, native speakers or not.) I think comfort with the language leads these students to believe that this manuscript-writing business will be easy, that a paper can presumably be thrown together like their college writing assignments. When I return heavily edited drafts, they seem to be quite annoyed with me, much more so than international students.

I am not a native English speaker, but I speak and write English well. What is most important is that I have considerable experience with technical writing (manuscripts, proposals, abstracts) and it is safe to say that I am competent when it comes to reporting science in written form. Furthermore, I am an educated person, and have written my fair share of essays in my native language and several others. Best practices regarding the structure or length of a sentence, punctuation, and flow are not restricted to English. Last but not least, as the lead senior author, I put my reputation behind each paper, so ultimately what I say goes; I would prefer not to be crass about emphasizing this point, but it seems to elude some people.

I would like the student to trust me on the best practices in technical writing, even if they feel that their freshman-year English composition teacher would kill us both ... or that they know better because I am some English-as-a-second-language ignoramus.

Why Your Advisor Takes Forever to Edit Your Paper

The most common reason for a delay returning nearly finalized manuscript drafts to students is a missing or inadequate "big picture," coupled with painful under-citing. I edit the text mercilessly and extensively; generally, edits to the technical parts of manuscripts do not take me long to complete. What does take a long time is to create a proper and compelling introduction, with adequate coverage of the literature and the exact positioning of our contribution with respect to the state of the art.

The questions of why we do what we do, what we do that is novel, and why anyone should really care get visited repeatedly during the course of the project, well before there is publication-worthy data. The student reads many, many papers, we investigate different approaches, weigh the pros and cons, take detours and go on tangents, and talk extensively. The big picture should never be lost in the advising process and I think that faculty, regardless of discipline, will agree with me on this issue. We would all like to think that we try to instill in our students the bird's-eye view of the research, along with the ability to look into the nitty-gritty details. One without the other is not good training.

I have weekly group meetings and we often talk about the strategies for writing better papers. I am sure I am totally annoying as I constantly repeat my spiel on the importance of citing and proper explanation of the motivation behind our work. We also often talk about efficient strategies for quickly mapping out the state of the art in a field through identifying key papers and then following their citation branches, while weighing the outcomes with the offspring papers' age, citations count, prestige of the journal, quality of the group, relevance to our own work, etc. Generally, before a student ever sits down to create the first draft, we have talked about the outline — what the paper is about, what its message is, why it is important.

Yet, this particular part — writing an introduction well and with ample citations — does not seem to stick. Even my best students, who are technically stellar and I know have read the relevant literature, give me initial drafts with a measly single "background" paragraph, in which barely 10 references have been thrown together to supposedly introduce the work, with generic, sweeping statements that beg for a citation, but, alas, none is to be found. It is as though it is too tedious to position oneself and the student can't wait to get to the fun stuff — their own technical contribution.

A good introduction is like a vortex: it starts from a broad view of the field, then narrows down seamlessly to important and open problems, so that by the time the reader is hit with the "In this paper …" there is no doubt in the reader's mind that what is being presented is new and extremely important.

So why does it take forever to return the nearly submission-ready drafts? Because I am the lead senior author, so if the paper sucks, it's my reputation on the line. I have to make sure we didn't miss anything among the new developments, that we have paid homage to the important contributions of yore, and to make it as clear as possible why we did the work and where it fits within the field. Even after multiple back-and-forth revisions with a student and major rewrites of the whole text, I do considerable clean-up right at the end: a full literature check and multiple overhauls of the introduction and abstract.

My Darling

I am working on a paper that I think has the potential to be a really big deal. I am so excited to finish it and submit it that I literally can't sleep. I sometimes (probably more often than I care to admit) feel like I'm falling in love when it comes to papers or proposals, with butterflies in the stomach from all the anticipation. I can't get my darling paper out of my head; I keep thinking of the softness of its curves, the color of its data markers, the size of its axis labels … *sigh*

Maybe I need a cold shower.

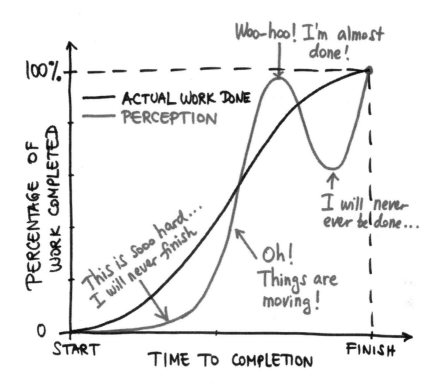

Let It Flow — Part 1

Reader J asks how to ensure good flow in technical writing:

"I'm going to be a graduate student soon. I follow your blog, especially when you talk about writing, because I'm not good at it. A problem I have had since middle school is that my sentences and paragraphs don't flow well. My papers are "hard to read." As a nonnative English speaker, I also have to edit manually for parallel sentence structure, comma splices, and prepositional phrass. I have some good references for sentence structure and phrases, but how do I write smoothly?"

First, I want to commend J for being conscientious about writing well so early in his or her career. This will make J's advisor very happy!

I am not a professional writer, editor, linguist, grammarian, or anyone who has any degree or certificate that would attest to any sort of formal qualification whatsoever to speak of good writing in English; in fact, I am not even a native speaker. What I do have is over a decade of being a professional scientist, publishing independently, writing grants, and training others how to report science in written form. I will share what I do and why.

Technical Writing: Not Unlike a Competitive Sport

In general, technical writing is relatively formulaic, and you can write passable research papers even if the prose is stilted. However, the quality of writing — good versus excellent — will make the difference between getting published in a middling versus very good journal, or between getting denied and getting funded. I highly recommend working toward getting as good as you can. The good news is that you can become considerably better at technical writing — especially in regard to aspects such as composition, flow, and writing speed — by practicing in a medium such as a blog or a personal journal, where you can experiment with breaking the grammatical and stylistic rules (e.g., playing with punctuation, emphasis, choppy versus lengthy sentences, how the choice of a synonym changes the tone of the whole sentence). If you were an athlete, you'd be cross-training; swimmers lift weights and run, for instance. Consider blogging or keeping a journal a form of cross-training for your main sport, which is technical writing.

What Is Flow?

Grammar and proper sentence structure should *never* come before good flow, good tempo, proper word choice, and whatever else it is that you need to get your main thing across. In technical writing the "main thing" is your point, i.e., your main finding. (In nontechnical writing, the "main thing" might be to advance the plot or to convey a character's emotions, for example.)

So please don't let yourself obsess about grammar, at least not in the initial stages of writing; that's something to worry about once it's time to edit (more in Part 2). I will take a student's draft with poor subject–verb agreement or repeated adjectives any day, if the text flow is good and if they write in a logical and persuasive manner.

What's good flow in technical writing? You essentially want the reader to follow your train of thought, starting from certain easily grasped or widely accepted facts/laws/phenomena, through linked statements, to your "main thing." Good flow means that a member of your audience can keep a relatively constant pace of reading, without having to pause and reread a cumbersome construction or jumping ahead to skip redundant paragraphs. Ideally, the only places your reader stops are where *you* want them to stop — where there's a figure, or an equation, or a spot in the text where something is being emphasized. Flow means that you hold the reader by the hand and they walk comfortably beside you; they have enough time to notice and enjoy the flowers. You should not be lagging behind the reader, which would mean you are being redundant or spending too much time on trivialities, and you should not be dragging them behind you, which would mean that they often have to go back and reread hard-to-parse sentences. (Notice the redundancies in this paragraph? For instance, I could have cut the whole walking metaphor.)

In technical writing, good flow also means that you will recognize the places where your reader might ask, "Wait a minute, what about this?" You should ask that question for them in the text, right at the point at which they would ask it themselves, then immediately give them a satisfying answer. Good flow means your reader can be sort of lazy while enjoying the fruits of your intellectual labor.

What helps with good flow? As with all things writing, what helps most is reading. By reading a lot of technical papers, you will find those that you feel have been particularly well written. Pull them aside and dissect them. Apply the scientific method: Ask why you think this paper is so well written, what makes it so appealing? Try to figure out what the moving parts are. Trust me, it's much easier to do this for papers than for grant proposals; I am still convinced that good proposals contain magical pixie dust.

Also, read your own writing. I like to reread my own papers and proposals (blog posts, too!), even after they have been submitted or published. I read them many times during the writing and editing processes, and these rereads help a lot with the flow. Sometimes I think my students don't read their papers at all before sending me drafts, because I can't believe they would not have caught how constipated some sentences sounded if they had actually read the thing through.

Your Weaknesses Need Not Be Your Undoing

If you are a nonnative speaker of English, you might be self-conscious about your command of the language. My university has pretty good English-as-a-second-language courses aimed at graduate students, and these do help correct gross errors in writing and speaking. But you ultimately want to write at a level similar to that of a comparably educated native speaker, which means that you should not be happy with just avoiding egregious mistakes; rather, you should continuously refine your spoken and written English.

My own big grammatical issues are the use of the definite and indefinite articles, as well as prepositions, because the information that these words carry in English is conveyed through the use of cases (forms of nouns) in my mother tongue. My Chinese students sometimes have issues with the English tenses and the use of gendered pronouns, again because the information about the when and the who is expressed differently in Chinese. Students with different backgrounds have other systematic problems when they write, depending on the language of origin.

Trying to speak and write like an educated native speaker means using idiomatic English. I like to experiment with idioms and even funny novel constructions, such as puns, and experimenting means that sometimes I get things wrong. I have certainly flubbed an idiom (or a hundred), but you have to use them boldly in order to get better. Pay attention to the word choice of native speakers; I always note when someone uses a phrase that I probably would not have used or that I don't really know the meaning of, and I make sure to look it up.

Finally, don't assume that just because someone is a native speaker they are automatically a superior technical writer. In grad school, I was getting ready to apply for faculty positions and had my two best American friends check my research and teaching statements. The two were not consistent about what they wanted fixed, not even at the level of whether a noun needed an article or not in front of it. So don't assume that you suck just because you are a foreigner; conversely, don't assume you're automatically golden if you are a native speaker (your nonnative-speaking advisor will thank you).

Another issue, which holds for native and nonnative speakers alike, is that people seem to have certain personal stylistic tendencies that are not ideal. I tend toward too many transition words and sentences that are too long, and I tend to repeat myself. On the blog, I edit more or less thoroughly, depending on my mood and available time; some posts are better than others. Sometimes I leave the redundancies because I am lazy or because I liked a paragraph and just didn't want to cut it — blogging is a hobby, after all, so I allow myself to get messy and self-indulgent. But, in technical writing, which is my professional mode of communication, I am very serious about cutting redundancies, removing the superfluous *moreovers*, *therefores*, and *howevers*, and shortening sentences for maximal clarity.

All this is done at the editing stage, though, which means you already have a rough draft ... So let's talk about how to get from a dreaded blank page to a draft you can polish.

Let It Flow — Part 2

Thy Paper Shall Have a Story

Before you write a paper, ask yourself:

1. Do you know what you did?

2. Do you know why you did it?

3. Do you know what you found?

Most students know what they did, which in a paper goes somewhere in the methods section and is often easiest to write.

However, most students, especially junior ones, don't actually know *why* they did what they did, other than that their advisor nudged them toward it. The "why" is at the core of your introduction, a very important part of the paper. A poor introduction often reveals that you don't really understand where your work fits within the state of the art, which in turn means that you have to go back and read the literature more broadly, and you have to talk to your advisor more.

Understanding what you found goes into the results part of your paper. That's "the meat." Students have an easier time writing up the results than the introduction, but I often find the results to be written trivially, just reading curve trends off graphs. That's generally not enough for any reputable journal.

Your paper has to tell a story. It needn't be the world's most complete story, but it has to have a beginning, a middle, and an end. In other words, it has to have the Why (Introduction), the How (Methods), the What (Results), and the So What, i.e., how it all fits with what we know or don't know (Results/Conclusion). This is the paper's skeleton, and it's a good idea not to start writing the full paper until you have all the parts. (You and your advisor should talk about the skeleton several times.)

Once you really, truly understand the why, the other parts are easier to write. The introduction needs to help the reader recognize where your field is and what the important open problems are, explain what you do to address an open problem and how you do it, and connect this background to what you found along with why it's important.

Here is a general outline for a good introduction (each of the following paragraphs can be split into two or more if there is a lot of material):

Paragraph 1: Open with an overview of the state of the art in a broader area and perhaps note certain technological applications.

Paragraph 2: Recent developments in the relevant subarea; what is known (who measured/calculated it), what is still being debated (who said what, if there are competing experiments/theories) or what is relatively open (any relevant work, perhaps on related systems), and why it is particularly important that we find an answer to some of those questions. (This paragraph also mentions briefly some of the common experimental or theoretical methods, as you discuss the work of others).

Paragraph 3: "In this paper/letter, we ..." State concisely what you did. It needs to connect to the open problems you just discussed as important in the previous paragraph. State what you did, how, and what you found, and how it answers the question(s) posed in Paragraph 2.

Paragraph 4: Comprehensive papers in the physical sciences usually contain a "Table of Contents" paragraph, where you say things such as "This paper is organized in the following manner.

In Sec. II, we present the methodology, ..." Many people keep it entirely generic (Sec. II Methods, Sec. III Results, Sec. IV Conclusion), but I like to put in more detail and use this paragraph to show how the main thread connects my story ("In Sec. III A, we present the results of neutron-scattering experiments on vibranium ... In Sec III D, based on numerical simulation, we reveal that the unique mechanical properties of vibranium make it an ideal material for intergalactic warfare").

The Vomit Draft

The whole paper — the material you put in and the order you put it in — is in the service of presenting your story. The story should be reasonably clear in your head before you start writing. But sometimes, after you start writing, you actually go and look some stuff up and think of things another way and, all of a sudden, you need to change parts of the story, perhaps dramatically. This is natural — it happens in technical writing, as well as in fiction — and is perhaps the most fun part of writing: the fact that writing helps clarify your thinking. Which brings me to the common saying that you make figures first, then write around the figures; this is true enough, but is hardly gospel. I say have a skeleton first, a decision on what the paper will be about (informed by dozens of figures you and your advisor already went through before writing), then make the figures to best support your story, and *then* write the results section around the figures. My students and I redo the figures many times during the writing/editing process, as we distill our message.

However, you have to start somewhere, and that somewhere is a reasonably clear concept of your paper's story. (Sheesh, have I said it enough times already?) Then you start writing a rough draft, also sometimes colloquially referred to as the vomit draft, because it hints at people vomiting the inside of their heads onto the page; like vomit, the product is generally misshapen and not pretty, though it is usually not smelly. (If your vomit draft actually smells like vomit —eeww! — stop spilling food all over your keyboard. You are gross.)

Occasionally, I hear that some people don't write a rough draft, but their sentences come out of their heads perfectly formed, with no revisions necessary. I don't really believe this, but if it's true, more power to them. Most people need a rough draft, which they then edit, and for them *it's good practice to separate writing* (which helps with the flow) *from editing* (which ensures that horrible grammar, spelling, and punctuation are not unleashed upon the world, or worse — your advisor's desk!).

So, with a clear outline of the main story in your head, just start typing things as they come to mind, *as you would tell them to another person*. Imagine yourself giving a talk … unless giving a talk is even more terrifying than writing, in which case imagine you are on a beach, in a hammock, talking to a really hot hammock neighbor about your research project over some margaritas. At this point, please don't worry about grammar at all. Just write how you think about your story.

A trick that helps is to start writing amid a block of already existing (unrelated) text, so the whiteness of the page isn't daunting. I always refer to the movie *Finding Forrester*, in which an old writer helped his young protégé by having him type on top of an old story. This trick has helped many a student. In my group we use LaTeX, so everyone starts learning LaTeX by working from someone else's paper anyway, which provides examples of both LaTeX commands and of semi-related prose wherein the students can nestle their drafts.

The point is to start; once you start, just dump the contents of your mind onto the screen. Write as things come and, as long as words pour out of you, don't stop … unless you are starving, have a bladder that's about to burst, or can barely keep your eyes open. In any of those cases, please stop; you will be able to get good flow later, I promise.

Don't worry about "the muse" in technical writing. You will get good chunks of text written on multiple occasions. Just write. It needn't be pretty, it needn't be super organized, just write. Consider it a chance to reveal your thought process, your knowledge, and your excitement to other scientists. The more you write, the lower the barrier to writing.

Edit Later

Popular culture erroneously depicts the ability to write as some sort of mystic, hard-to-replicate experience. What is even worse is that nobody ever shows editing, an absolutely critical part of the writing process.

Write first, edit later. But when is this fabled "later"? When the flow stops. When you are done with a few paragraphs. When you are having a hard time getting the flow started. When you are almost done. When a few days have passed since you finished a draft. When an office mate asks you to look at their paper. When it's either edit or check references. Basically, don't edit at the level of every word or every sentence you produce, but you can do it paragraph by paragraph or page by page or section by section, depending on personal preferences, available time, and editing stage.

Good editing means careful reading, putting yourself in the reader's shoes, and — more often than not — murdering your darlings (cutting sentences or even paragraphs that you like but that don't work in the context of the whole piece), so your other darlings can go on and get reviewed well at a fancy journal.

Don't be afraid to relax some stylistic rules to ensure good flow. For example, sometimes long sentences are justified and work better than several choppy, shorter ones. Don't be afraid to use punctuation in the service of your point: I use commas, dashes, and parentheses, which can all help separate a minor clause, depending on how closely it's tied to the main clause. I love the semicolon and use it a lot in technical writing; it provides closer coupling between successive sentences than a period. (Sadly, ellipses and exclamation points are not welcome in journal papers.) Proper punctuation will help pace your reader.

Happy vomit-drafting!

This Bean-Devouring Leprechaun

Technical writing may be largely formulaic, but there are still traps to avoid. Here are some of my top technical writing peeves:

- Don't start a sentence with an abbreviation, i.e., don't write "Eq. (3) can be simplified ..." or "Fig. 5 shows the dependence ..." At the beginning of a sentence, always write out the full word instead: "Equation (3) can be simplified ..." or "Figure 5 shows the dependence ..." Abbreviations are fine elsewhere.

- Compound adjectives need hyphens. For instance, it should be "a well-deserved honor" as opposed to "a well deserved honor." However, "the honor was well deserved." In both cases, "well" qualifies "deserved," but in the first example both "well" and "deserved" together form a compound adjective that further qualifies "honor."

- If hyphens start to make you dizzy, such as in "the 5-nm-wide ribbon," consider rephrasing, such as "the width of the ribbon is 5 nm."

- Commas are your friends. Commas make the world a better place. Love them, use them.

- Don't use "this" or "that" as the subject in technical writing, i.e., don't write "We report that the leprechaun fart rate increases cubically with their bean-consumption rate. This implies that leprechauns should be kept on a bean-light diet." What does "this" refer to? The fascinating bean–fart relationship? One of the many nouns in the previous sentence? Something like "This dependence implies ..." works well. Maybe I should start adding "bean-devouring leprechaun" after "this" or "that" every time I catch this type of mistake.

- Your paper is not a poisonous reptile. It will not hurt you if you get too close. Do not keep it at arm's length, where you write in a detached manner and rely heavily on the passive voice to remain noncommittal. If you hate your paper, it will hate you back, and the reviewers will hate both of you.

- Statements should be kept emotion neutral, especially if they refer to the work of others. You can say that your approach is more accurate or has a wider range of applicability than the approach of Joe Schmoe et al., but don't say things like "Our approach is vastly superior to that of Schmoe et al. because they only relied on this lowly/simplistic/old-fashioned approximation." Also, while it is wonderful that you are excited about your research, you can't say things such as, "Amazingly, we found that Schmoe et al. had it all wrong."

- Don't say, "To the best of our knowledge, [...] has never been done before." It's just silly — of course all you wrote is to the best of your knowledge; there is no need to explicitly say it. The statement sounds like a self-deprecating preemptive apology in case you missed something and the referee gets upset. It's your duty to do the most comprehensive literature survey that you possibly can and then stand behind what you consider to be the state of the art.

- Don't be lazy with references. One of the most common complaints I have regarding the writing of my students, even those who write compelling technical prose, is under-citing.

- I hate "impact" used as a verb. I'm not sure why, I just do. I hate reading about stuff being "negatively impacted" by the leprechaun-turd production. I had a collaborator who savored it, in contrast to the perfectly legitimate "to influence" or "to affect," for instance, and it was driving me crazy. Then again, I used to feel passionately against "thus," but have developed a tolerance to it. And I hate it when people take liberties with abbreviating journal titles as they see fit and not as they are standardly abbreviated. I am passionate about the serial comma.

- Always write with an audience in mind. The readers are not inside your head; they don't think about this problem of yours all the time, like you do. Just because you found a specific analytical derivation, computational intricacy, or experimental protocol particularly daunting and were proud of yourself for surmounting this obstacle, that does not necessarily qualify said obstacle for a central position in your paper. The 20 pages of details that are only ever likely to be read by a poor grad student entrusted with reproducing your data can nicely fit in an appendix or in online supplementary materials, rather than in the main body of the paper. Lead with the motivation and insights that your audience can understand and appreciate; this is key to creating enthusiasm about your work.

- When I spend many, *many* hours editing your excruciatingly comprehensive paper in equally excruciating detail, and then you give me the next version in which large chunks of text have been untouched, so I have to do it all over again, I might bite your head off. It is very easy to keep your head, though: simply enter the needed changes when I first request them.

Stephen King's *On Writing*

I had never read a Stephen King book until I picked up his *On Writing: A Memoir of the Craft*. I can tell why the man has sold millions of books. *On Writing* is part memoir, part writing advice, and I couldn't put it down! I can only imagine how his thrillers read ...

I had never read anything by King because I have always had this vague impression that he was a horror guy, and I really cannot read or watch horror; if I do, I can't sleep for days, like a total baby. I saw the movie *Carrie* and a few others of his, like the show *Under the Dome*, which only solidified this preconception that his writing would be too creepy for me. Plus, in the interest of full disclosure, I have heard from several people close to me that his books are shallow. I think I will have to re-evaluate both my own snobbery and that of the advice givers.

King grew up lower middle class. He was raised by a single mother and knew nothing about his father. Both he and his brother were highly intelligent and managed to finish college despite the economic hardship. While they struggled financially and King worked a number of pretty grueling, low-wage jobs starting in high school and well past college, into his family-building years, he had support for his craft at home from an early age, which indicates that his mother was an open-minded and educated person.

It's interesting why he wrote this book. The answer comes from a conversation with his friend, the novelist Amy Tan, who said that popular writers like them were never asked "about the language," i.e., about their craft. As if penning a story that sells is orthogonal to good writing; as if being able to connect with millions of people, book after book, is not an extraordinary gift worth understanding.

It turns out that King is very passionate and very serious about his craft, and has a lot to say about it. He insists on lots and lots of writing and lots and lots of reading, and himself writes daily with a 2,000-word quota. He subscribes to the Strunk and White "adverbs are evil" mantra, and has strong feelings about grammar and vocabulary. He connects writing a story to unearthing a fossil. I was amazed to read that he doesn't plot the story out; he throws the characters together and sees what they do. I found this liberating. King also says he doesn't believe in a traditional muse; to him, a muse is a grouchy middle-aged guy with a beer gut, whom you need to teach that he has a job to show up to daily, during regularly scheduled writing time, and eventually he will.

King argues that a lot of damage has been done by people insisting that substance abuse is inextricably connected with creative work; he posits that maybe there is a higher incidence of abuse among the creative types, but that it doesn't matter, as everyone looks equally disgusting puking their guts out. He had a period of near-constant drunkenness and drug abuse, which ended shortly after an intervention by his wife and friends. By the way, throughout the book, his love and admiration for his wife, writer Tabitha King, shines clearly and brightly. It is quite sweet and was thus unexpected (to me), considering his propensity for the grim and the gruesome.

Let me wrap up with a few insights that are pertinent to a life in academic science:

- Once on a project, King doesn't stop writing unless he has to; otherwise, the characters go stale in his mind. I can totally relate, but this is not an option for us academic writers at all, or anyone who's not self-employed. There are many situations in which I wish I could go on writing papers or proposals, but other work and family obligations require I drop it. Ah, to have the gift of large blocks of time to write.

- "If there is any one thing I love about writing more than the rest, it's that sudden flash of insight when you see how everything connects." Need I say more?

- He recommends writing the first draft with closed doors and quickly, fueled by enthusiasm and fast enough to outrun any self-doubt. When the first draft is done, have your Ideal Reader read it (for King, it's his wife). Then leave it for at least six weeks and go work on something else. Afterward, read, edit, and send to a larger pool of no more than a dozen friends and colleagues. This is excellent advice for technical-paper writing, but especially for grant proposals. If I could write a proposal and then have it sit for six weeks before it's time to submit, and if I could routinely count on friends to read and give me feedback (instead of never, now that I am a grown-up scientist), that would be amazing.

- Perhaps the best insight from the text has to do with King's desk. For years he had this massive desk in the middle of his study and was, in his words, "drunk and stoned" behind it. After he got clean, he got rid of the desk, purchased a smaller one, and put it in the corner. The rest of the room was then furnished as a family area, where his kids would come to hang out with him. The desk size and placement are a metaphor: "Life isn't a support system for art. It's the other way around."

Chapter 8

Peer Review of Papers and Grant Proposals

Your Paper Is Really Boring

I am late with my review of a paper for *Reputable Society Journal.* I am the tie-breaker referee and have been trying to do my duty diligently, really go through the paper with a fine-tooth comb, analyze the response to each of the other two referees, and carefully weigh the pros and cons for the publication of this paper.

The problem is that the paper is really, *really* boring and I am not convinced that it should be published at all. I have picked it up and put it down several times. I don't think there is anything wrong with the technical part of the work; I believe that it's been competently done and that it is correct (within the constraints of the techniques they use, of course). But the overarching question is: why, oh why did they do this work? And, more importantly, why, oh why did they write this paper? I mean, the work is topical, it explores a sort-of-hot area, but the authors ask questions to which we actually already know the answers, and write the paper in a way that doesn't really reveal anything, new or otherwise.

I have read the paper several times, and I still have no idea what the conclusion is, what one is supposed to take away from it. I know as much about this topic after having read this paper as before, I am just older and wearier. The paper does represent a huge amount of work, but other researchers would have probably done something more appealing with the data than the authors did.

There should be a reason to write a paper, *any* paper. You might try to solve an existing open problem; you might identify a flaw in how things were previously done and do it better or differently, so that new features are revealed; you might identify an unexplained phenomenon, and offer a hypothesis explaining it, with as much proof as you can muster; you might attempt to prove or disprove an existing hypothesis ... Whatever you do, *your paper should tell us something about the world that we didn't know before*. It's your duty, as the author, to frame this story for the reader. We need to know what you did, why you did it, how you did it, and what the point of all that is, i.e., what we are supposed to remember from your paper.

In this paper, I know what they did and how, but I don't know why and I don't know what I am supposed to remember, as the portion that resembles a conclusion is pretty trivial. Sometimes, not coming across as a jerk referee is a tall order.

In Defense of Tardy Reviewers

Tardy reviewers are a pain in editors' butts. One might rightfully ask why someone would agree to referee a paper and then be several weeks late.

Being an author, I totally understand and agree. But, being a sometimes-tardy reviewer myself, I feel I also need to speak in defense of my deadline-challenged brethren. We are very sorry to be late. We really mean it. We should certainly write an email to the editor, saying we need additional time. We actually say yes to a request to review because, upon cursory inspection of the paper, it appears interesting and within our field of expertise. We don't get much (if any) benefit from reviewing a massive number of papers every year, but we value journal review as an important service to the scientific community and are willing to put in the time. However, even with the best of intentions, life intervenes, and because paper review is a service activity with no recognition for the reviewer, it often gets demoted as people need to reprioritize.

I was recently on vacation and took a couple of papers to review with me. During the vacation, I got several more requests, of which I declined all but two. One was for a short paper, which I reviewed promptly; the other was for a longer manuscript, which I left for after the vacation. When I came back, there was a major "fire" that needed putting out: a large collaborative grant up for renewal. The work on the grant proposal had to be done right then, because two big players were about to leave the country the following week, one of them for a whole year. No paper review happened that week despite my good intentions, but neither did some other important things, such as meeting with several of my students who got stuck with their projects while I was away.

One could say it is just plain rude to say yes and then stress out everyone else by not delivering in a timely manner. I agree, but ... If people said yes to a review request only if they were 100 percent certain they could deliver by a given date, the editor would likely have to ask 20 people to get two to say yes; that alone would take a very large amount of time. Wouldn't you rather have an occasional reviewer late? Remember that reviewing is an important service, but also a time-consuming activity that does not benefit the reviewer, so, yes, it will get lower priority when more urgent stuff comes up. Ironically, when you are a reliable reviewer, editors tend to pile on you, so you end up being late. Personally, I would much rather my paper be reviewed by the editor's first or second choice, even if the review is late, than the editor's 15th choice, because by that time we are likely moving far away from referees with the desired expertise.

When I was a student, I was always upset about late reviews of my papers; now that I review nonstop, I no longer am, as I know what's going on. I am that reviewer who writes you a lengthy report. Actually, I spend much more time on the reports for manuscripts that get unfavorable reviews than for those I liked, because it's important to give people something to work with to improve their papers. When I look at how long it takes me to get the reviews back and how long I take to return them, I feel that the duration of the actual technical review correlates with the size of the paper (shorter papers review faster), time of year (high season for travel or not, proximity to proposal deadlines), and the quality of writing (if the paper is poorly written, it can delay the review, as the reviewer will likely try reading it, get annoyed, and just leave the manuscript for later, again and again. Writing a nice, readable paper will increase your chances of getting the review back promptly).

Review duration also correlates with reviewer seniority (big shots get more requests). To enhance review speed, editors of some journals recruit more junior people (e.g., postdocs) as referees, because they are less busy and more likely to review in a timely fashion.

While I no longer wish all the worst to tardy reviewers, as I did as a student, I am still quite aware that publication speed makes a significant difference for the career prospects of students and postdocs. It is often favorable to choose a fast journal over a sluggish one, even at the expense of a couple of impact-factor points. What does vary dramatically among journals is how long it takes the editor to make successful referrals and how prompt he/she is about making a decision once the reports are back. Editors who are practicing scientists have some of the best turnaround times I have witnessed.

Editorializing

I edited a special issue of a journal in my field. The special issue focuses on the topics in which I am an expert, so I know virtually all the contributors (at least the group leaders) fairly well. When soliciting reviews, I tried to contact postdocs and junior faculty about as often as I did senior people. This being a special issue means I had to deal with a large number of papers over a fairly short time span and on a small number of topics, which has revealed some interesting patterns in the review process.

My initial guess was that younger people, postdocs and junior faculty, would be less busy and more likely to accept to review, would accept or decline a referral more promptly (this journal provides an accept/decline option), and would overall submit their reports faster than the busy senior folks. Here's what I found:

Bar none, the fastest review (and a very detailed, to-the-point one) came from a well-known, well-respected, and presumably very busy senior person in the field. In fact, several of the very prominent people, whom I was reluctant to even ask for a review because they likely have multiple review requests from different journals on their desk at any point in time, were very prompt in accepting to review, and were either on time or just a tiny bit late with their reports. These reports were always professional, detailed, and very useful.

So, should we conclude, "When you want something done, get a busy person to do it"? Hold on, not so fast. Unfortunately, among the people who took the longest to even respond that they would indeed review, senior faculty were also the most numerous. When it comes to referee responsiveness, the senior-folks distribution is tail heavy.

I am quite puzzled by how many people take forever to accept or decline to review. I have never understood that. You read the abstract, and then decide whether or not to review, and click on a link. How hard is that?

I don't mind people declining to review, but I really appreciate it if they do it promptly. Unfortunately, postdocs and junior faculty have actually been much less likely to accept a referral for papers clearly within their expertise than I had hoped. I know that junior people are not idle, quite the contrary. My guess is that they don't want to review because they feel there is no immediate benefit to their careers from review, but I think that is shortsighted. Becoming a well-regarded reviewer improves your standing in the field and keeps you at the forefront of your specialty. Junior people should have a light review load, but I think it's important that they do it. It is part of training and part of being a good member of the scientific community. Being a sloppy or disinterested reviewer, while presumably expecting others to pull their weight on your behalf, is certainly not going to enhance your standing in editors' eyes.

There is one person who submitted two papers to the special issue. Yet, I was unable to get a single report out of him after multiple reminders. I would think that it's only fair that if you want others to review your papers (note the plural) you should pitch in.

Another interesting question is whether to indicate that the paper you are reviewing is missing citations to your own work. In the case of a special issue, we are dealing with a focused set of topics, so this problem came up several times. I found that most people had no qualms about requiring that their papers be cited, and generally rightly so, even though when the list of papers to cite contains only those from a single group, it becomes fairly obvious who the reviewer is.

We all want our papers reviewed promptly and thoroughly — I cannot imagine anyone wanting their paper reviewed slowly or sloppily — but many people provide exceedingly terse reviews or are so late that the referral has to be withdrawn. We often fail to treat others the way we would like to be treated ourselves.

Revision Trumps Rebuttal

I just received a revision of a paper I had previously reviewed. I gave them a very positive and enthusiastic first review, but required that they do two things, which I knew they could do, as some of the authors had done them before on similar systems, and which I knew would require a few weeks of work; the cost of the additional work was not onerous, as it's computational. They came back not having done *anything* to the manuscript. They wrote a response in which they argued that what I had asked them to do was a great idea and something they should ideally do, but that it would take too much time (I disagree) so they just didn't want to do it right now.

A word of advice to anyone who will ever submit a paper for peer review: you should not expend all your time and energy on the response letter arguing with the reviewer. If you don't want to or cannot do what was required, then do something else instead. You have to make *some* edits to the paper in response to what was required. A comment, a reference, a paragraph of discussion along the lines of what the referee requested and why it is a good idea in principle, but not right now and might be done later.

How can I accept your paper when you have made absolutely no edits whatsoever to it? It's as if my first report never happened.

Err on the side of revising rather than rebutting.

Propeller Referee

It's a good idea to occasionally remind myself and the many jaded likes of me that peer review is a worthwhile endeavor, and that we should perhaps all work on our own refereeing karma by really trying to help improve someone else's paper (and perhaps, on occasion, our own mood along the way).

I often referee for *Prestigious Society Letters (PSL)*. It is a very good journal, well respected and with a long tradition. *PSL* papers are usually interesting and very well written, because they ought to be appealing and accessible to nearly all physicists. A common type of declination from *PSL* is of the type, "This work is nice and well done, but of too narrow a focus (or not interesting to anyone beyond the niche area or not accessible beyond a small subfield and unlikely to be improved by rewrites), and should be sent to a more specialized journal instead," which would be the *Reputable Society Journal (RSJ)*, with several subfield-specific flavors, published by the same society.

I am sure I reject *PSL* manuscripts as often as the next referee. But, a while ago, I was sent a paper written by a couple of relatively junior scientists. As I went through the paper, I started getting excited, as the authors were really onto something novel and unexpected; unfortunately, it was almost entirely buried underneath layers of poorly structured writing. I submitted the report to the effect of, "Interesting work, and the most exciting aspects are this, that, and the other. However, as it stands it is unacceptable, but I expect to be able to recommend publication if you rewrite and reorganize so as to make it more appealing, and this is what you should do ..." I followed with a list of detailed suggestions, such as, "Move this part here, de-emphasize this and emphasize this instead because that's what really counts, this was original and novel so bring it forward, cut this completely, put this and that in the abstract, move this to discussion, etc." I rephrased back to them what I felt was the most important and novel thing in the paper, and how I would phrase these key issues if it were me writing the paper.

A couple of months later I received a revision. I saw the report of another referee, who had tersely said that there was nothing novel and it's not *PSL* worthy. The authors responded in detail to both our reports. They revised the text along the lines I had requested and it turned out absolutely great! The same work, the same data, just written differently, and it looked very, very exciting, with a crisp and powerful message. I was happy to accept right away after that resubmission, but wondered if they still faced an uphill battle with the other referee who had previously flat-out rejected them. A month or so later, I see that the paper has been accepted and that the second referee basically said, "Wow, I now see what is novel and important and agree this is *PSL* material, so go ahead and publish."

Karmic brownie points notwithstanding, it felt really good to propel the good work of others.

Panelicious

The proposal-review panels at the NSF run for two days. The first day is spent going over each individual proposal. Each panelist has reviewed a certain number of proposals; how many depends on the number of submissions and the number of panelists. Each proposal must have at least three reports, but often they have more. The reports may come from some of the panelists or from ad hoc reviewers. One of the panelists who reviewed a given proposal summarizes the proposal for others and leads the discussion on the proposal's merit. Another panelist, who typically did not review that proposal, acts as a scribe and takes notes on the discussion. By the end of the first day, it is pretty clear who the top contenders for funding are and who has no chance, with a few as "maybe," although I have never seen a proposal from this category move to "highly recommended" (i.e., likely funded). The second day is spent on the final rankings — deciding who among the top contenders actually gets funded — and on cleaning up the panel summary statements, which have to be agreed upon by all panelists.

The low funding rates — a measly 10 percent in my division — make the proposal-review process appear stochastic. Yet, every time I have been on a panel, there was one proposal that you could bet would get funded just by flipping through it. It was polished, everything was in its proper place, the figures were pretty, and the whole document was aesthetically quite pleasing. This outward attention to detail also manifested itself inside — the proposal was meticulously crafted. When you run into the Great Polished One, you instantly recognize it, and it always gets funded.

But there are typically several more that have nearly everything: a great idea, preliminary results, a competent PI, a good plan, no major flaws in how the proposal was organized or written, no major qualms about anything technical ... Yet most of these will unfortunately not get funded.

Here is the stochastic part of the review process: The success of your proposal hinges on your panel, and its composition is different each time. In my directorate, it is unheard of to address the comments of a previous panel formally — you can incorporate changes to your proposal, but nobody writes a summary of changes made in response to a previous panel.

On a recent panel, we could have easily recommended for funding three times as many proposals as there was money to fund. Two-thirds of these will get tossed and have to try their luck next time, with the next panel. The worst destiny is that of the proposals ranked just below the cutoff; I was in that situation not that long ago — close, but no cigar. With the next panel, such a proposal may easily end up in the "not recommended" category; the fact that it almost made the cut last time means very little.

So, what decides who actually gets funded in this seemingly stochastic process? Panel composition and interpersonal dynamics.

1) You have absolutely no chance of funding unless someone on the panel decides to champion your proposal. How do you ensure this happens? Obviously, your work should be interesting, relevant for the program to which you submitted (talk to the program directors if you are unsure where to submit and what types of proposals they want), and well written. This is essentially all you can control. Other than that, you can suggest potential reviewers and those you would like excluded, but I am not sure how much program directors look at these suggestions. It probably varies from director to director, but my guess is they probably at least take a look, even if they don't actually invite the suggested researchers. It is even better if more than one person champions your proposal.

2) You have no chance of funding unless the person championing your proposal is doing their task well. You have to provide them with enough ammunition to fight off the attacks of other panelists, who support other proposals. This is under the assumption that your champion is knowledgeable enough to be able to fight for it with real arguments and that they have the tenacity and energy to persevere. Which brings us to ...

3) You will not get funding if the person championing your proposal is too nice or meek. Panel dynamics are always the same − there is a loudmouth who attempts to have the last say and is supposedly an expert in everything. Too often I have seen nice people back down because someone boorish and aggressive has made them start to doubt a good proposal; the aggressor may not even have a point, but the aggression, combined with the human propensity to back down when a sliver of doubt emerges, can reduce the funding chances of perfectly decent projects. Your champion may also be defeated in a sheer battle of wills − some people simply don't like confrontation, and will back off because they don't feel it's worth their time and aggravation. This is what has always angered me − the proposal championed by the biggest jerk on the panel generally gets funded because most people are nice.

4) You should not worry too much about points 1–3, as you have no control over them. Just make sure you write the best proposals you can and volunteer to sit on review panels to improve your grant-writing skills. Without a doubt, partaking in panels is the best way to learn how to write grants. It helps you see what people respond to, what others in your field propose to do, how good proposals are organized ... You also get to learn something new and you get to flex your debating muscles.

Panella Bread

What can I say? I love stupid puns. You know, panels fund research, feed people ... Plus there is actually a Panera Bread in the food court across the street from the NSF.

I was recently on a panel at an NSF directorate to which I don't usually submit proposals, but which is close to my expertise. It was an interesting experience.

The funding rate is about twice that of my division. That made all the difference in the tone of discussion. On this panel, we were actually able to fund all the proposals that were considered not to have major flaws. In contrast, on the last panel in my division, the fight was very vicious about getting to pick n, instead of $n+1$, for funding.

It is natural to consider a PI's track record, and it is human to be a bit star-struck when reading a proposal by a Big Shot. But, in my division, if a person is extremely well funded, that generally reduces their priority. Not so much in this other division — we ended up funding a person who had a dozen active grants. I must say that it left a bad taste in my mouth to give the precious and scarce NSF funds to someone who commands such immense resources already. Some panelists were saying, "But look at the track record!" Well, yes, the PI has a veritable army at their disposal; why don't we just forgo panels, take the money and distribute it to the most prominent names at the top-five schools, and be done with it? I am sure those guys would find some use for it.

There was a significant difference in the proposal layout. Prior NSF support, a necessary ingredient of every proposal, is just a pro forma blurb in my division, and is usually in the back of the proposal. In contrast, there are several pages of detailed description of prior work near the beginning of every proposal in the other division, even if the proposal didn't really rely on prior NSF work. This was an interesting and unexpected aspect.

Another difference is the broader impacts. In my division, questions always arise about why there isn't something specific to the actual proposal that the PI will do for broader impacts, something new. It is not considered sufficient to just keep doing what you are already doing. In the other division, when I brought this up, I was quickly told that it was not fair to ask people to do more when they are already doing enough. Overall, the broader impacts in my division are considerably more detailed and I would say stronger than in this other division.

One thing I liked at the other division's panel is that the panel seemed more likely to give an exciting topic a chance, even if the proposal was not perfectly written. In contrast, I cannot say that I have seen a proposal get funded in my division that wasn't exceptionally well written.

Apart from the differences above, the panels functioned in pretty much the same way, with the panel going over the proposals and producing a rough ranking on the first day, and the second day devoted to the final ranking and the clean-up of the panel summary statements. People argued for and against proposals; it was lively and interesting. We were all exposed to a lot of very nice science.

Overall, serving on the panel at the other division was a nice experience that opened my eyes to some unexpected differences between divisions. This experience emphasizes that the best way to learn how to write proposals that a certain program will fund is to get in touch with the program director and offer to serve on their panel.

Chapter 9

Giving Talks and Networking

On Presenting Research Data

When I was a graduate student, I lovingly pored over every single figure that contained my data. Each of my presentations had a really clever title page, with a unique picture that was a pun or some sort of twist on the talk title. I spent a lot of time adjusting the timing and sequence on every animation, aiming for the perfect pitch. I constantly changed the color scheme, the font type and size, and, as needed, even redid the figures to accompany my grand vision. In hindsight, I wasted way too much time tending to these presentation aspects (my advisor was pretty hands off, so his input was minimal).

Once you become faculty, the sheer amount of stuff you need to present per unit time goes up dramatically. You give many, *many* talks, of varying length; you can have 2-5-minute poster teaser presentations, 10-30-minute contributed talks, 30-45-minute invited or plenary talks and seminars, as well as variable-duration presentations to funding-agency representatives. Collaborations also become the norm, and you often present not just your own group's work, but that of your colleagues. Sometimes, those colleagues don't send you their materials till the night before the talk.

Doing things as quickly and efficiently as possible becomes very important, so you simplify and streamline, often at the expense of visual appeal. I now have simple guidelines for making figures and presentations, so that I can quickly take bits and pieces from different sources and still throw together a decent-looking conference abstract or a talk in virtually no time.

When it comes to presentations, I use variants of a simple, neutral template (there are still some frills on the title page, but not many) and a simple, widely available sans serif font (Arial) for all presentations. While serif fonts are great for printed matter — the serifs help you visualize and follow a line — they make my eyes hurt when on screen. I am also not a fan of bright letters on a dark background. My text is black on a white background; if something needs to be highlighted, it's either in a red or blue font. I keep animations to a minimum as presentations often need to be printed as handouts (such as for grant reviews) or in case I have to use someone else's computer.

I also have clear and simple guidelines for making publication-quality figures and I request that my students follow them. Everyone in my group uses the same software to plot figures, so tried-and-true best practices are highly transferable: this is how large your axis labels, tick labels, and legend font need to be, and these are the preferred line colors and thicknesses. We discuss the layout of figures in group meetings and brainstorm on how data should best be presented. When it comes to two-dimensional (2D) plots, I insist on a simple color palette of black, red, and blue; it works well for most 2D plots. The software we use also creates awesome three-dimensional plots and movies, which we often use in presentations.

Students often start by disregarding these guidelines because they feel they know better about how to make their data look all "purty." That's not necessarily bad, but with new students we invariably have to go through the territory of having a figure with, for instance, red and magenta curves (*recoils in horror at the color clash*) or the very common issue of completely illegible lettering on the figures once they are shrunk down to the size they are in print (society journals we publish in have a two-column format with figures about three inches wide). I understand that the students feel ownership of the data and feel they can do better than some stupid template, but it is exhausting having to hash it out with each one of them that a simple color scheme with appropriately scaled lettering goes far, and that they don't have to reinvent the wheel. Getting students to accept these best practices is part of mentoring, but is certainly among its more tedious aspects.

ROBIN HOOD'S GUIDE TO GRAPHING

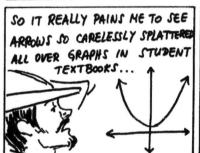

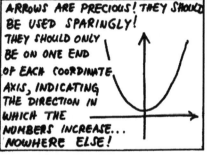

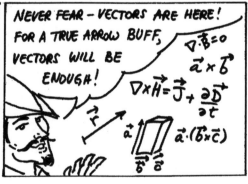

XYKADEMIQZ 2014

Giving Talks at Meetings

I am very comfortable teaching. I can move about, gesticulate, and draw on the board. I can see the faces of my audience clearly and can gauge whether something is sinking in or not.

In contrast, I find giving talks at meetings fairly stressful, as the very act of delivering a talk is uncomfortable. I don't really suffer from stage fright; instead, I find it's mostly the external constraints that ruffle me.

First, you are always at the mercy of the organizers in terms of which computer you use. Most places nowadays you can use your laptop, but not always. The logistics of giving a talk can also be really weird. I remember a meeting where the talks were projected onto these giant dual screens that are great for the audience, but the speaker stood to the side and below, seeing one of the screens, on which he or she was supposed to point at stuff, at a ridiculously small angle.

A related issue is not being able to move around. Sometimes you have to stand near a stationary microphone, as opposed to having a portable one that attaches to your clothes, so you can't really peel away from the lectern; luckily, this issue is not very common. I love using the gadget that helps you remotely advance slides, and which would in principle enable you to stand wherever you like and give the talk. However, it may or may not have a very long range (the range tends to scale with price). I sometimes forget to bring mine with me or to put in fresh batteries, or I simply chicken out as I get too nervous about moving around like a crazy person when everyone else stands nicely in one spot and delivers their talk.

I am also not equally comfortable pointing to the stuff on my right and my left, and am very uncomfortable pointing to stuff behind my back. I remember a talk I gave in this weird room with a couple of very large, nested, U-shaped desks, where the audience sat. At the common opening of the U made by the desks was the screen. The speaker could only move into or out of the U, perpendicular to the screen, and if they were facing the audience, the screen would be behind them. It was unbelievably awkward and impossible to point at anything without turning your back to everyone else. The only way to avoid having your back to the screen while facing the audience was to stand really, really far to the side, where people could barely see you and you'd be uncomfortably close to the people sitting at the ends of the U's. And this was a high-stakes talk, given to a committee that was supposed to encourage or discourage a continuation of our funding. It remains the most uncomfortable talk of my life. We did get the money, which I suppose is what matters.

Finally, when you give talks at meetings, the audience is typically in relative darkness. You sort of see the faces of the people who are *not* paying attention to you, as they are being lit by the screens of the laptops on which they are working instead. Sadly, you see much less of the audience members who are actually listening.

Give me a nice classroom full of fidgety undergrads any day!

How Do You Know That Your Talk Didn't Suck?

I recently came back from a trip during which I gave several talks (actually, several incarnations of the same talk) and met many people in more-or-less similar fields.

When I give talks, I am acutely aware of my audience. If the talk is sinking in and the audience is engaged, it is immensely inspiring and I feel it further improves my delivery. If the audience is ambivalent or hostile, I start feeling very uncomfortable, and I believe that it hurts my delivery: my jokes fall flat; I catch myself backpedaling and overall seeming desperate, which generally just makes things worse. It doesn't help if there is someone I am trying to impress in the audience; if that person does not seem particularly enthusiastic, I can get discouraged pretty early on. Yes, some of us professors are sensitive little flowers, wilting at the sight of an arched eyebrow.

Even though I gave basically the same talk several times, I feel they were quite different in quality. The first one was OK, the second one poor, the third one good.

I never have enough time to practice the talks. It's a fairly common ailment of faculty — talks are generally finalized on the plane, in the hotel the night before, or even during the talks preceding yours. When you have experience teaching and give dozens of talks a year, the baseline quality of talks is passable even when you don't practice. My main issue when giving talks without practicing is that I tend to get long-winded and go overtime, which are among the most grievous of academic sins. On the other hand, I have also found that over-practicing kills my will to live and makes me give dull, uninspired talks. It seems I inherently lean toward improvisation.

Giving talks is a performance art. I think anyone can get reasonably comfortable with presenting, but some people are naturally awesome at it. They have the right combination of confidence, eloquence, and wit to accompany the technical material, presented in a visually appealing fashion. The rest of us range from not-so-awesome to disastrous. While there are obvious things that one can do to make a presentation better — e.g., don't overload slides, especially not with text or formulas; go easy on animations; practice — as usual, a lot hinges on the intangibles, like simply having charisma. I would put myself in the "decent presenter" category, with most talks rated OK. I also appreciate the transient nature of talks and cannot imagine wanting to have myself recorded for posterity — imagine the time sink, having a video (or videos) of myself that I could go back to dissect and obsess over, ad nauseam.

It would probably be awful if someone came and told me my talk was bad; I prefer fearing that it sucked over the certainty that it did. I recently gave a talk where some of my students were in the audience; while we discussed how everyone liked all the other talks, we didn't discuss mine — I don't think they would feel free to give me their honest opinion, and I didn't want to make them uncomfortable, although I would have appreciated feedback. Based on my experience in my very macho field, asking for any kind of feedback from anyone is a sign of insecurity, so it's just not done once you are considered a grown-up scientist.

On Communicating Science

During my undergrad days, I received an old-fashioned, butt-kicking education, with a heavy emphasis on mathematics. In hindsight, it also involved a number of educators who felt the students were there to feed the teacher's ego. If you, the student, did not understand something during the lecture, it was communicated loudly and clearly that the reason was that you were stupid and unworthy. Teachers being bad was not even a possibility, because they were to be unquestioningly revered, regardless of how ineffectual they were in practice. Naturally, my classmates and I adopted this attitude that speaking incomprehensibly was the way to convey that you were smart, and that smart people didn't ask questions.

Then I came to the US and I met brilliant people who asked questions I would be embarrassed to utter for fear of looking stupid. I met teachers who did not mind patiently answering even the silliest-sounding queries. I discovered that very smart people did not have to rely on obfuscation as a means of asserting intellectual superiority, and that true mastery of a subject was more often than not accompanied by clarity in conveying key points. I started appreciating building intuition and finding examples, "guessing" what should happen before rolling up my sleeves and firing off the heaviest mathematical artillery.

My work spans topics from very mathematical to very applied. The very applied projects are considerably easier to explain to a general scientific populace, while the heavily theoretical ones are not for the faint of heart and are not easily discussed with broader audiences. However, over the years, I have learned that no matter how complicated and abstract the topic is, it is possible to convey at least some of it to a fellow scientist in another field if you really want to. But many people don't consider it important to think a little more broadly about the context of their work, about how parts of their effort connect to adjacent subfields or other disciplines.

Early in my career, I was guilty of similar sins, giving conference talks about the minutiae that excited me. At one point, a senior colleague came up after my talk to tell me that I didn't show them the forest, only the trees. I felt offended and defensive, but he simply said, "You can do it. You can do better." I'd like to think that these days I give engaging talks, which a variety of people are able to follow.

Yet, every so often I do get reminded that a number of people still equate incomprehensible with difficult or important. A few years ago, I was at a conference that is a theorist's paradise. While I could follow all the technical details of the talks, I realized that most of the time I didn't actually want to, because they were unbelievably boring. I want to be able to remember key points from the talk: what the problem addressed is, why it is important, what the speaker did and roughly how, and what the overarching message behind the finding is. If I want a step-by-step exposition, I will talk to the speaker afterward or download and read the paper.

The ability to engage an audience is not a trivial skill. It is also the difference between getting funded or not, between getting invited back to give another talk or not; it means being effective in the classroom and drawing enjoyment from teaching people who are awake and attentive as opposed to not. We can all do better.

How Do You Like Your Conferences?

Every graduate student should experience a conference with several thousand attendees at least once. However, I find these meetings to generally be a poor use of the large amounts of money that are needed to attend them. They are held in expensive locales, in large conference centers, with people staying in pricey hotels. The high registration fees don't cover much, so one still has to pay for all meals, which are also costly because, again, the whole event is in an expensive place.

These days, I like to go to small and focused conferences, with no more than roughly 200 attendees and a single-session format. At this size, you can make personal connections and have real, technical conversations, which can result in long-term collaborations and science friendships. With a relatively narrow topic and single-session format, you are actually interested in and following most of the talks, as opposed to checking email or browsing the web.

Beyond that general preference, what do I like in a conference?

1) **A well-made program, with interesting talks, especially invited ones.** At large conferences, the organizers usually bring in big names for plenary or keynote talks, but seeing these prominent folks is cool in the same way seeing the Rolling Stones play live is cool — sure, you should do it once in your life, so you can see the legends and brag about it, but it's all entertainment and you won't get to meet Jagger anyway. Indeed, these big names usually give their well-flowing overview talks and leave shortly thereafter, so they don't talk to many people and don't actually do much for the community that came to hear them.

In contrast, at a conference I recently attended, the organizers did a very good job with the selection of invited talks: many went to relatively junior, very active people. They were assistant and associate professors who gave good and engaging presentations, stayed the whole time, followed the program, and mingled with the other attendees. This is good for the speakers and good for the community.

2) **The single-session format, with plenty of time to talk with people.** I like to go to a conference to listen to the talks and chat to other attendees, largely about work. Ideally, I want to be able to listen to *all* the talks, and not have to run around between rooms. A conference is a good use of my time and money if there are engaging contributions in every session and I want to be there the whole time. Conferences where I end up spending most of my time in a hotel room because I don't care to listen to anyone are a waste of my time and money.

3) **When I go to a conference, I go to work; I do not go to have a vacation.** This appears to be a difference between me and many people, also a difference between the young me and today's me. I don't want an exciting or expensive place. I want cheap registration that provides a lot for the money; I want an affordable hotel that is close to the conference venue so I can easily get something from my room if needed (like a sweater if the conference room is freezing); I want an engaging technical program; and I want a lot of opportunity to interact with other attendees over food or coffee.

I do not want to skip the talks to go sunbathing or swimming or skiing or sightseeing. I want to work and think and extend my professional network, and, honestly, boring but comfortable places where the attendees end up spending a lot of time together (in no small part because there is not much else to do) work great.

My ideal conference is organized at a university campus in the US. Why? Large lecture halls are excellent auditoria for the talks, with appropriate video and audio equipment, enough electrical outlets for all attendees, and reliable Internet access. The lecture hall can usually be booked for free or very cheaply. There is often affordable university lodging close to where the conference takes place, with restaurants and bars in the surroundings. Due to cost savings on venue rental, plenty of food (breakfast, lunch, coffee breaks, and dinner, if possible) can be included in the registration fee, which makes for very happy attendees.

Finally, a conference is really successful if you come back home with a bunch of new ideas.

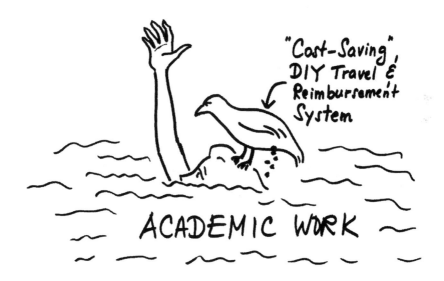

Musings on Networking

Presenting work at conferences is an important part of being a scientist. It falls under the broad umbrella of making your research known to the scientific community. Being able to create and deliver a good presentation is an inherent part of graduate and postdoctoral training.

Let's say you are a junior scientist — a graduate student or a postdoc — and you are attending a conference. Generally, your primary purpose is to present a paper (otherwise it would be considerably harder to justify your expenses to the university financial services and therefore harder to get your trip reimbursed). You present a paper and hopefully do a decent job. The probability of having a talk versus a poster depends on the field and the particular conference. In some communities, posters are looked down upon; in others, poster sessions are a very important mode of interaction among the conference participants. If you have a talk, ideally you practiced in front of your group members at least once — the so-called "dry run."

So you survived your talk or poster session. What do you do the rest of the time? Are you alone at the conference, without anyone you know? Do you perhaps have some of your group mates around? Is the whole group attending, including your advisor? If there are other group members around, you may even go together to do some sightseeing. But it is important to actually take advantage of the technical program and attend the talks and poster presentations of other people whose work relates to yours.

Whether you are attending by yourself or are there with a group, conferences are your chance to meet other scientists and enhance your professional network. Networking is considered a dirty word among many academics, who seem to viscerally reject it as being a gauche corporate term for schmoozing, something that the presumably intellectually pure, ivory-tower dwellers needn't engage in. In my opinion, it just means meeting people, getting to know them, and generally trying to be kind to them, whoever they are. Some small fraction of the people you meet may turn out to be professionally useful to you. Others, not so much. But spending a few minutes chatting with someone need not be torture.

Like any group of people, scientists vary in their social prowess. Still, I think it's safe to say that people in the physical sciences are not considered beacons of congeniality. These days, however, you cannot be an extremely successful scientist without at least average social skills. For instance, I know a very successful young professor who would come to a conference with a list of people he wanted to meet, and he literally would not rest until he'd met every single one of them. He is supremely energetic and charismatic, probably on par with the best advertising executives, lawyers, or businessmen. He also happens to be a very creative scientist, and this combination of extroversion and technical excellence is a great recipe for success in today's show-me-the-money science model.

Most other scientists are more introverted or not quite as charismatic. Still, networking is necessary, unavoidable, but with practice, it can become bearable or even fun.

The best way to make good professional connections is to attend small or midsize meetings, like workshops, where the attendees have a lot of opportunity to interact with one another. After a few years of showing up, people will start recognizing you and saying "Hi!" Even if you feel awkward and totally out of place the first (or second or third) time around, showing up repeatedly will make people used to you and you might actually start feeling like you belong there. What I would recommend for a junior scientist, from grad student to tenure-track faculty, is to identify two or three small-to-medium conferences, where it makes sense to show up every time. It is the best way to find a community where you will be comfortable, and where you can feel supported, both in the abstract sense and in terms of having future collaborators, or just general connoisseurs and proponents of your work.

You don't have to force it. There are plenty of relatively low-effort opportunities for networking at conferences. Every conference has some sort of an opening reception, most have a banquet near the end, and there are poster sessions, coffee breaks, and lunches. These are all chances to talk to people, if you feel like it. I completely understand not wanting to talk to anyone and just wanting to have your lunch or your coffee in peace. But try not to spend 100 percent of your breaks alone or with people you already know. Even if you aim for meeting one new person per every weeklong conference, that's still something!

When you are alone at a conference, if you pay attention, you will see that there are always tables with people who also seem to be there on their own. You can certainly sit at one such table and try to start a conversation. Usually it works, sometimes it doesn't, but it's no big deal. The point is to meet someone new, practice small talk, talk about what you do, hear about their work, and then move on. The art of moving on is also very important and something that even many senior folks have yet to master — reading the cues that the interaction has run its course and you should go your separate ways, and not taking it personally.

Many people are very discriminating when it comes to chatting with people at conferences. Both junior and senior people are often guilty of bending over backward to talk to someone they perceive as important, and don't think twice about ignoring those whom they consider lower on the totem pole, unimportant, or generally unremarkable (a student, a postdoc, a woman they view as someone's accompanying person ...). I have often been on the receiving end of people assuming that I am no one of consequence, usually because they think I am a student or someone's wife, although the former becomes less common the older and fatter I get. I generally correct people or assert who I am, and it doesn't bother me too much unless it's really egregious. One example of a blatant slight was the guy I met at a recent grantee meeting for a federal agency. We were all walking up to the cafeteria and I was talking to a big-shot graybeard from another institution with whom one of my former undergrads is now a grad student. This other guy came up to us, looked me over like I was the shit on his shoe, wedged into the conversation, then quickly screened me out by first passing by me, then starting to walk right in front of me so I had to slow down, and finally completely cutting me off from the person I had been talking to. You bet I will remember this guy, but not fondly.

It is basic decency to talk to anyone like they are a worthwhile human being. But when it comes to forwarding their professional agenda, many people seem to forget this rule. So perhaps it's useful to rephrase it in the professional networking context: talk to everyone as if they matter to your agenda, because you have no idea when a certain connection or a certain 10-minute chat may actually materialize into something that benefits you. It is never a bad idea to be kind to another person. I personally don't mind small talk; people usually like to talk about themselves, and I like hearing their stories and learning something new about different universities and areas of research. So I just go on autopilot along the following lines: I ask about the university, how large it is, what they do for research, how large the group is, if they come to this conference often, what some other important meetings in their field are. If they are a professor at a public university, I may ask about state support, department size, if they have had recent hires, and what the tenure process looks like. Then we might kvetch about funding in general or discuss where each one of us gets funding from. If they are a student or postdoc, I ask what they do, how far along in their program they are, what they plan to do when they graduate, and where other people from their group have ended up. If I happen to talk to someone's spouse, I ask about the city they live in, how their trip was, if they have stuff planned for after the conference; sometimes we talk about kids, which I enjoy. When you think of it, the whole small-talk business is quite formulaic, and thus hopefully less intimidating. The point is that it should not be hard to spend a pleasant 10 minutes talking to pretty much anyone and learn a little about them. Being a listener is an excellent quality for making connections with other people.

Forget about sucking up to the big guys and hang out with your peers. Everyone always tries to chat up the big shots, who might meet you but will usually forget you, especially if you are junior, unless they know of your work (i.e., they know your advisor) or you have been introduced to them by an elder (i.e., they know your advisor). It's also quite amusing how much many of the big shots enjoy all the attention … but I digress. So just hang out with people your own age. Making friends with other young folks is not only easier when you are a student or postdoc, but those young folks are your actual peers. They are the future leaders, and those conference connections of today are the collaborative proposals, grants, and postdoc placements for your students of tomorrow.

Finally, you don't feel like interacting with other humans? Then don't. If you are painfully shy, too busy, temporarily not in the mood to talk to people, or generally misanthropic, that's fine. You have my blessing to keep to yourself; there is no need for torture.

But ... if you don't actually mind talking to people, I would say just relax and talk to whomever seems interested in talking to you. That's all you need to do; that's networking.

Following Up with New Connections

Let's say you met some interesting people at a conference or a grant-review panel. How do you follow up with them? The answer depends a little on what type of interaction you had. With some people you just had a nice brief chat, but you didn't connect either professionally or personally. I would say you don't have to follow up with them at all, but be friendly if you ever meet them again.

If you connected with someone personally, like if you are both grad students and went bar-hopping, then just do the usual friendly stuff: email, text, Facebook, tweet. Whatever feels comfortable.

But if you clicked with someone professionally, if you do similar research, keeping in touch is actually quite easy, because scientists are huge geeks in the best sense of the word: they are enthusiastic about their work and *loooove* to find someone else who shares their passion. In this case, a few days after the conference, I usually send an email saying something like this (unless I get a similar email from the other party first!):

"Hi New Science Buddy,

This is Sydney Phlox from the University of New Caprica. It was a real pleasure to meet you last week at the 15th International Conference of Awesome Physics. I enjoyed hearing about your research on superawesome spins and ultra-awesome laser pulses. As promised, I am sending you a PDF of my presentation, as well as the preprints of the Glamour Magazine *and* Reputable Society Journal *papers that I mentioned when we spoke; they are about to come out in the next month.*

Optional 1: Invite them to come give a talk at your place, such as, "Would you like to come give a talk at UNC? Our seminar series is on Tuesdays. If you are interested, send me a few dates that work." If they tentatively invited you to their institution and you really want to go, you can throw it out there and say "About me coming to give a talk at your place, I could do mid-April or early May. Let me know which dates would work. Thanks again!"

Optional 2: Insert joke about weather/sports/food in exotic locales/travel/something not entirely technical that you might have discussed.

Best wishes/regards,

Sydney Phlox"

When someone I know sends me their papers, I *always* at least briefly take a look; based on anecdata, I think that most people do, too. I have several colleagues with whom I have a relationship where we will just send each other our new papers that we think the other one might find interesting, accompanied by a few pleasantries and general information about life (for instance, if you send your new papers, you might also add that you are moving institutions). Then, we hang out whenever we meet at conferences again, but usually not extensively, just for a few meals or coffee breaks. With a few colleagues, the relationship has become a tad closer, in that we will actually send each other emails to the effect of "Long time no see, what have you been up to?" In that case, mentioning that you got married or pregnant or that someone close has passed away would probably be OK. A couple of my European colleagues send me Christmas cards. With a few I have an open invitation to come and give a talk whenever I am in Europe, which I did take advantage of once or twice.

Also, if you see the other person's new paper in a journal, that's an excellent excuse to ping them. ("Just saw your paper in *Nature*, congratulations!") The same holds if you see they won an award — be happy for them and let them know you are!

Overall, try to keep it friendly and light, perhaps a little aloof. You certainly shouldn't push anything.

Chapter 10

Colleagues, Collaborators, and Academic Politics

GETTING INTO THE RIGHT
FRAME OF MIND BEFORE
THE FIRST FACULTY MEETING
OF THE NEW ACADEMIC YEAR

XYKADEMIQZ 2014

Choosing Collaborators

Usually you hear "people, not projects" in the discussions on how grant dollars should be distributed. Recently, I came to think how the syntagma holds for collaborations.

I have long-term collaborators with whom I really enjoy working. Our collaborations may not be continuous, but they are frequent, as we often apply for funds together. I like how they think, how they work with students and postdocs, and their attitude toward science and toward publishing. I also like them as people. However, there are a number of colleagues whom I like as people but with whom I think (or I know, because I tried) that I wouldn't enjoy working.

If I like collaborating with someone, I will work with them on pretty much any topic to which it makes sense to apply my expertise. From the good interpersonal chemistry comes good science, as people amplify each other's contributions. The back-and-forth discussions are constructive, the insights build upon one another, and the whole result is really much more than the sum of its parts.

I also have a perhaps unusual quality in that I get along fairly well with several people who are considered difficult by some colleagues. Maybe I am difficult, too. For instance, I worked very well with my PhD advisor, who was notoriously aggressive and unpleasant. After I had become a professor, for years people would ask me how I survived working with him, to which I said it was no problem and that we worked very well together. The trick was to understand what brought about an overreaction from him and work around it. At my current place of employment, I work very well with several people who are considered volatile. I have no problem with them, either. I have found that my cultural background helps in that I don't expect people to be infallibly jovial. I consider them to be humans, which means that they have a right to be tired or anxious or pissy or happy, as long as they are engaged with the work. It seems that difficult people relax and don't freak out around me because I don't freak out around them. Note that there is a difference between professional but grumpy/sad/angry and unhinged or abusive or petulant. Nobody should have to tolerate the latter, while the former is a normal part of close interactions. I find the ability to relax and just be yourself around someone to be absolutely key for the free flow of ideas and long-term collaborations.

My favorite collaborators have similar work schedules to mine — they work a lot, often long and unusual hours, and are generally always available to talk science. Email conversations often happen after 10 p.m. We make joint work a priority. When I have an idea, I am not afraid to run it by them. They respect my theoretical work and seek my input, and are willing to try experiments if I have an interesting hypothesis. They treat their students and postdocs with respect and give them a lot of autonomy, and they show respect by placing a high value on their students' and postdocs' success — publishing a lot and well, engaging junior people when writing proposals, sending them to give invited talks. A favorite local collaborator of mine is probably in his late 60s or early 70s and has one of the coolest groups I know. They are all unbelievably loyal to him, and he treats them with warmth and humor. I hope to be like him when I grow up.

Collaborativignette

I have two collaborators whose long-windedness sends my blood pressure through the roof. When I see an email from either one of them, I know it's not going to be under two full screen lengths, with paragraph-long, epithet-laden sentences. Being that I am a very impatient person, I get really ticked off. If you want to send me an email with your stream-of-consciousness ruminations, such that I have to scroll and scroll and scroll, please, for goodness' sake, call me on the phone instead and save us both some time and, in my case, copious gastric acid.

One of these collaborators is junior and I am wondering if I should tell them that their wordiness is something they really should work on losing.

Collaborative Paper Writing

When I work on a manuscript with only students or postdocs as co-authors, there is a lot of back and forth as I edit, we talk about the edits, they correct what they can, rinse and repeat a few times. That's how students learn to write papers. Eventually, if the paper is not in acceptable form after several iterations, I just take over and rewrite it. The students/postdocs can and do give input on my rewrite, but the structure does not really change after I have rewritten it and I basically have the last word on how the paper looks.

Working with multiple senior collaborators is trickier. Each of us professors thinks of himself or herself as the greatest writer ever, and we all have huge egos in general. Most successful faculty are fairly decent writers, but there are undoubtedly differences in the writing style, and many, *many* faculty have surprising pet peeves and hang-ups about the writing process. People have strong feelings about punctuation, figure layout, use of transition words, you name it. In contrast to working with students and postdocs, there is no clear hierarchy as to whose word gets to be last, and while people nominally think that all collaborators are equal, they never really are.

For instance, on papers with experimental collaborators where I do the theoretical work, an experimental collaborator is usually last author, and the paper will be recognized as his baby. So I submit my theory write-up and any data/figures that are needed, I give comments on the whole manuscript when solicited, but I don't really stress over how the whole paper looks (aside from making sure it's correct) because the other colleague is the lead, with the responsibilities and perks that come with that status.

It is much trickier when I feel that I am the lead but the collaborator does not share this sentiment, as in the cases where we nominally do a similar amount of work, but I end up pulling significantly more weight, so I feel my word should be last. I used to have one such collaborator who, despite contributing significantly less in time and effort to the project, liked to have the final say. That aggravated me because I felt like a postdoc — I do the heavy lifting and the other person just slides in as a conquering hero to make the finishing touches. But, I like having things done in a timely fashion more than I like having my way. So the student who was the lead junior author and I iterated until the paper was essentially ready for submission, at which point we sent it to the other professor, who made the cosmetic edits, and we submitted. That way everyone was happy — the student and I were happy because things got done fast, and the collaborator was happy because they felt they had the final say. I was last author.

Collaboration Dissolution

How does one get out of a collaboration that doesn't seem to be going anywhere?

All of my collaborations that have dissolved because they stopped functioning were simply abandoned to die by all (dis)interested parties; at some point, no one attempted resuscitation any more. We stopped communicating and went on with our lives, never discussing what transpired. The upside is that there was no confrontation, so everyone is technically still on good terms. This is not a bad thing in the long run.

I also have several collaborations that are generally healthy, but are on-again, off-again, depending on available funding and interests. We work together, go our separate ways when the grant ends, then rejoin a few years later to do something else. I like this type of collaboration. I enjoy working with these people, as they have the same zeal for publishing and attitude toward student advising as I do, but we don't have to be joined at the hip. In contrast, I have some colleagues who do everything collaboratively; I would find that stifling.

Are you and the collaborators you want to leave on a grant together? If not, then just cut your losses and part ways. If you are, then you need to produce something for your own sake, even if the collaboration is not working out. Proceed as best you can alone. If it feels appropriate, offer to include the collaborator on papers on your own terms; if they don't agree or are being difficult, that's your answer. I have found that even very demanding people, when you do all the work and offer to have them as a co-author on a polished paper, will swallow their pride or whatever other bug they have up their butt and say, "Sure, go ahead and submit. Looks good!" I take myself off of papers to which I didn't contribute enough, but most people don't.

In Praise of Respectful Colleagues

Recently I had an email exchange with one of my favorite colleagues, who lives across the pond and whom I met a few years back at a conference. I have always admired his work because it is very insightful, rigorous, and to the point. When I finally met him, it turned out he was a serious guy, a deep thinker, who really wanted to talk with me about the science we both cared about. There was no pretense, no arrogance, just two colleagues talking shop. Over the years, I got to know him as a really good, solid person overall. We have stayed in touch about technical issues big and small, and I am really happy that he's someone on whose expertise and goodwill I can count.

Being a relatively young woman in a male-dominated field, my expectation from colleagues whom I meet for the first time, be it at conferences or when one of us is visiting the other one's institution to give a talk, is that they always start by assuming I don't know much and that I don't belong wherever it is that we are meeting. I am not sure people do it consciously, but they overwhelmingly do start by giving me these slightly annoyed, confused "What the heck is she doing here?" looks. As I get older and probably more confident, I would say most no longer think I am a student, but the confusion about what purpose someone like me has there remains visible. I am no longer irritated by this attitude; I just take it as a given.

Therefore, it always comes as a very pleasant surprise when a colleague I have just met treats me with respect and as an equal; when he (or, rarely, she, for there are very few women in the field) starts by assuming that I know my stuff and talks with me like one scientist to another. It should be the norm, but is an exception; when it happens, it always makes my day and restores my faith in humanity.

It would not take long to count the colleagues with whom the professional relationship started like this, with no drama. The people who are courteous, professional, and accepting are always the colleagues I would put in the category of the very solid, deep-thinker scientist, who does impactful work, but does not a priori go after the flashy fads. The rising or already bright stars generally (although not always) treat me as someone they can dismiss until I am proven worthy. I am amused by the change of attitude when it finally clicks that they have read my papers and that I am, in fact, not an idiot.

A while back, I read somewhere a good explanation of the difference between a geek and a hipster. A geek is passionate about something and is delighted that you share his/her passion; a hipster does not appreciate the unwashed masses messing with his/her big thing and will make sure to tell you that you are doing it wrong and should just get out. I think this distinction also applies to the scientists who are open and accepting (true geeks, in the best sense of the word) and those who are territorial and self-serving (akin to hipsters).

There is a field that I entered several years ago, and very soon thereafter I happened to meet two people, independently, who are really big names in the field. I had only begun working in it, so I was not aware of how well known these two were, but they were both very professional, very accepting, and basically really interested in what I had to say. To this day, I am always delighted to meet them, and one has become a good friend with whom I happily hang out at conferences. It all started just with them being normal, no-drama people.

So this is to all the wonderful colleagues out there who are passionate scientists and simply kind human beings, who treat all colleagues as colleagues, as knowledgeable equals, right off the bat: you are the ones who make science worth doing and fun. Thank you for being out there.

Political Skills in Academia

Political skills are necessary to become a successful academic. Otherwise, your chances of getting an academic position and thriving as a tenure-track and later tenured faculty member are slim, no matter how brilliant you are.

The political skills needed in academia could be loosely defined as the abilities to assess the balance of power and the hierarchy in your institution; to understand what motivates other people, what their agendas are, and where their loyalties lie; and to work within those constraints and the constraints of the broader academic system to advance your own professional interests.

All of the highly successful scientists I know are very good academic politicians: they are both technically excellent and they take full advantage of the relationships and the institutional structure to fulfill their goals.

Having political skills does not imply that you are dishonest or manipulative. Here are a few examples from the everyday life of an academic scientist:

1) You cultivate a relationship with a funding-program manager (this works better with some federal agencies than others). Your agenda is to get funding; the program manager's agenda is to find the best people to do the work for his program. You can listen to what the manager envisions and adjust your proposal goals to fit well with the program; it's a win-win situation. The opposite, politically unsavvy scenario would be complaining how nobody wants to fund what you want to do, without exploring what people actually want to fund.

2) Getting a stellar candidate in your area hired. Most tenure-track applicants don't realize how much intradepartmental politics shape the outcome of faculty searches. For example, the college will allow only one hire and often it happens that two subareas have a stellar candidate. So who gets to hire? Do the subareas join forces and call in favors with the dean and provost to work out a different tenure home for one of the candidates? Does one of the candidates get dropped? These are all possible outcomes, depending on the fine balance of power within your department, the department's relationship with the college, and the college's standing within the university.

3) You need lab space, as does Professor Labhog. Who gets it? It depends on your seniority, Labhog's seniority, and how much each of you is liked by the department chair or the people who have the chair's ear. There are aspects that can tip the scales in your favor (e.g., you are an assistant professor and need to start up your research program) or in Labhog's favor (e.g., he just received a large grant and needs the lab for the new project). How everything plays out depends on facts, as well as on your and Labhog's political skills.

These are all real scenarios where no malice is involved. Doing science requires infrastructure, financial and human resources, administrative support, and time. Pretending these don't matter is naive. Forming alliances over certain common interests (e.g., all faculty in one subarea want to hire candidate Rising Star) and disbanding to form others (e.g., while Labhog and you clash on lab space, you are on the same team to bring in Rising Star) are parts of the job. You have to be clear about your loyalties and your interests, and savvy about assessing those of others.

Spousal hires are an aspect of academic politics that inspires spirited debates. People object to a position being created for the trailing spouse and argue that, if such a position is created, a full search should be conducted and others interviewed as well. However, the number of positions is flexible. There are long-term strategic goals of departments and colleges, and perhaps a position was not a high priority at that particular point in time. The fact that there is an excellent primary hire with a spouse who would be a good fit for the other position means the position gets elevated priority — but *only* in the context of the spousal hire; otherwise, the resources would not be dispensed on it at that time.

A colleague of mine's spouse was a prospective spousal hire in another department several years ago. The spouse did not get hired because of strong opposition from a faculty member who sensed competition and lobbied against it. So the spouse took a job at another university, did a smashing job, and received early tenure; in the meantime, some college administration changed, and the now-tenured spouse with a phenomenal record was finally brought to the university. None of this would have happened without several layers of administration working together.

People ask whether anything but technical skill should be relevant — isn't academia supposed to be a meritocracy? I believe technical prowess is necessary for success in academia, but merit is not narrowly defined as technical excellence: a person who is oblivious to how the institution works cannot be successful. The rare lone genius is a remnant of a bygone time, if not a myth. Today's superstars rarely do the lab work themselves, but instead manage the students and postdocs and bring in a lot of funding, none of which can be done successfully without political skills. Should we not hire superstars, because their lab skills are probably rusty? Of course not. It is not just their technical expertise but also their political skills that enable the science to get done. Politics greases the wheels of science.

Academics are people, and political skills matter in all human interactions. Being able to understand what motivates each one of your staff is essential for having a productive group. I believe political savvy should be acquired through training, and should be an inherent part of a PhD or postdoctoral experience. For instance, students and postdocs should learn who the heavy hitters in the field are, in which direction the field is moving and who the new stars are, as well as where the emerging sources of funding are. We, as faculty, can share the experience and best practices not only in lab techniques, but also in how to market and advocate for oneself. Such skills would enable junior researchers to see the world of academia for what it is: a wonderful enterprise where challenging questions get to be answered to the benefit of humankind, but also a place where bills have to be paid, and favors have to be exchanged, and strings have to be pulled. This complexity does not make science any less fascinating, just more real.

Accolade Magnet

I am on a university committee that, among other things, selects the recipients of certain named awards reserved for the physical-sciences faculty of different career stages. It's a nice chance to peek at the CVs of successful people from different disciplines and see their career trajectories.

What caught my attention is a person I will call Accolade Magnet (AM). AM had been nominated for every award you can think of by their department and several professional societies, won most of them, and is universally adored. The letters of reference all but refer to AM as the second coming. I know AM some, and while I haven't had the chance to be dazzled by AM's technical brilliance, I can attest that AM is the nicest and most pleasant person you are ever likely to meet.

On the same day, I heard a fairly young faculty member, who also happened to be nominated in one of the categories for the university award, got elected as a fellow of a very selective professional society that I would never guess this person even belonged to, based on their field of expertise. Then I wondered whether another collaborator of mine, a deserving faculty and a much more obvious member of the same professional society, was ever nominated for the rank of fellow; it turns out they had been, but were rejected twice.

Many people are technically excellent, so that aspect alone means little. You have to be in the mindset of wanting awards, seeking them out, and getting people to nominate you or to write letters of support for you. Once you start getting awards, they keep rolling in. You have to be proactive at playing this game, and the game apparently gives back. Waiting to be nominated for anything based on, say, your excellent scientific output is naive. No one thinks of you because they are too busy thinking about themselves.

Young Administrator

I was at an event where a former faculty member, who had taken a fairly high administrative post at another university, came back to share his experiences about taking what he called the leadership path. This man is only a few years ahead of me. I knew him while he was still on the tenure track in a department different from mine. It hasn't even been a decade since his first appointment and it's only been a few years since tenure, and he already left a research career for full-time administration.

I went to the event to hear what caused him to make this transition. I must say that I always find it very curious when I see researchers actively seek administrative roles. I will probably have to be department chair sometime in the future, but I think that's still very far away, and I don't have the aspirations, political prowess, or people skills to do anything beyond that. I am neither patient enough nor eloquent enough to ever make a serious administrator, so I am always interested to see how and why some people decide to take this path. When a person is as young as this colleague, my curiosity is really piqued.

Faculty members in many STEM fields realize pretty early on that their job comes with a number of managerial duties. However, I think that a faculty job is still largely creative: having ideas and writing grant proposals; working closely with students on project design, execution, troubleshooting, and analysis; and writing up everything for publication. I expected that the colleague's new job would be largely administrative and I was interested in how he was able to satisfy the creative side. He said that he had always had a strong interest in teaching and outreach; he got involved in some broad education initiatives early in his faculty career and really devoted himself to them after tenure. He said that there was indeed a large managerial aspect of his current job, which is an administrative post several rungs above the level of a department chair, but that his creativity was being satisfied by developing the vision for the institution. He now has the freedom to affect the well-being of multiple academic units, which he would never be able to do as a faculty member.

He seemed genuinely excited about his work, drawing from a large pool of personal strengths, and feeling he was doing something important. He seemed happy with the job and optimistic, a man who has found his calling.

Meet-the-Speaker Paradox

When you are young and penniless, you may have a great need for credit, for instance to buy a car, or pay for school, or perhaps start up a small enterprise. But, being that you are young and without a lot of history, your creditworthiness won't be particularly high, which makes it hard to get a loan.

Fast-forward 20–30 years and you earn a good salary, you have perhaps paid off a house, college debt is history, and you have savings. Your creditworthiness is great and anyone would be delighted to give you a loan, for which you now have no need.

Professional attention is like credit — when you need people to give it to you, no one will. Once it is no longer important to you, everyone is racing to give you some.

Given this unfortunate fact, it can be annoyingly hard to populate the schedule of an early-career visitor. Sending out emails with the abstract and biosketch often results in very few people willing to meet the speaker. Then I have to send out individual emails, virtually pulling colleagues by the sleeve to meet with the guest. Other people do it, too, and I tend to relent when the host pleads that I see their guest for half an hour. It's challenging to fill up almost any speaker's day with meetings, but it's hardest when the speaker is a young assistant professor.

Therein lies the meet-the-speaker paradox: Professor Greybeard, who is exceedingly unlikely to benefit in any discernible way from visiting your illustrious institution, will have hordes of people wanting to meet with him and shake his hand and tell him how awesome he is and by-the-way-this-is-what-I-do. There will be standing room only at his talk, even if the talk is incomprehensible/boring/covers really old work. But for young people, whose careers literally depend on making connections and giving enough of these lectures, it is a real drag getting enough volunteers to populate the schedule. This is the main reason I have become gun-shy about inviting people over to give a talk. I don't want to host too many people in order to avoid wearing thin the patience of those colleagues who kindly agree to most of my meet-the-speaker requests. Having been very disappointed on occasion in the past, when I was the speaker, by very sparse schedules because my hosts didn't want to bother filling them, when I do invite someone these days, I go to great lengths to ensure the speaker is very busy throughout the visit, because busy means you are appreciated. You feel great at the end of an exhausting day, which you spent talking to many smart people about their science and showing them your own cool work. Maybe the young people's meeting worthiness isn't as stratospheric as Greybeard's, but I still like to treat all my guests like it is.

Musings on Departmental Politics

There are aspects of how an academic institution functions that only start to reveal themselves as you progress through the faculty ranks.

I have always thought of my department as fairly harmonious. I still think it's a pretty healthy department — there are no toxic feuds, everyone truly supports assistant professors, and there is nothing that would needlessly endanger the progress of a junior faculty member toward tenure — but I am now seeing that there is definitely a power clique and that things may not be all rainbows and unicorns unless you belong to it.

There is nothing particularly sinister going on; I suppose these are just my growing pains. When you are young and new, you are ready and willing to invest all your energy and enthusiasm into the department (or at least I was). You pour your little heart and soul into issues; you get supported, good things happen, and you feel great about your impact. But then you get a little too encouraged, and things start getting shot down. OK, you think, maybe you don't know what is going on and you are not particularly politically savvy, but you are willing to learn, and you do. And then you see that, in your supposedly democratic department, some things go through in spite of loud protests and nonexistent support, and you realize that people, some people in particular, don't actually care very much at all about what you have to say.

You hear that an excellent junior colleague of yours keeps his head down and doesn't participate in faculty governance because he, too, tried to give some input and was shot down by a senior colleague from the same research area with, "You are a kid. You don't know anything." So the excellent junior colleague is now lying low, keeping competitive, and planning to jump ship when the opportunity strikes. And the department loses a good person because some older loudmouth wouldn't listen.

Then you get some leadership roles and you think you are making a difference, only to realize that apparently you were chosen because a senior colleague, who you thought had your back, thinks you are easily manipulated. It turns out, they found your energy and enthusiasm amusing and oftentimes useful, but ultimately thought you were a gullible bumpkin.

So what do you do now? None of these issues is of great importance, but the accumulation of them simply makes you want to withdraw from faculty governance and mind your own business. You only have so much energy, and you want to save it for your family and students. There is no guarantee that any other institution would be any better and many would likely be worse. And you don't actually have it bad at all, if you only disconnect from politics.

Benevolent as the ruling clique may be (or they like to think they are), they do hold the keys to resources and promotions, so you need their support now and then. It is best not to engage with them at all, in order to minimize confrontation, so you can actually count on their support when you absolutely cannot avoid going through them.

You used to judge the people who ignore faculty meetings and don't participate in the life of the department. You can see their point now. The only scary thing is — what if the benevolent overlords are no longer benevolent? What if things get bad because everyone who could do something about it gives up, minds their own business, and lets everything collapse? Don't we owe it to the department to be present so things don't go to hell? Or do we owe nothing to anyone but ourselves, should stick around only for as long as it's fun, and once it's not, simply leave?

Shut Up

I really need to keep my mouth shut in faculty meetings. Or stop attending them.

When I go to faculty meetings, I tend to talk, because the stuff that comes up makes me want to chime in and I have a hard time stopping myself. But then I invariably feel bad afterward because I think I look like a fool. As my grandmother always said, "People will think you are smarter if you don't open your mouth." I say the things that I mean, and I know a number of others think them too, but they either keep their mouth shut or temper and qualify what they say to a palatable level. It goes to the whole let's-all-just-get-along attitude that is at the same time useful (we are, after all, supposed to be here together for decades) and very annoying (because people don't want to state their honest opinion and own it). My candor doesn't come across as very politically savvy among the colleagues who like to hold their cards close to their chest.

The Fourth Aspect of an Academic Job

There are three aspects to a professorial job: research, teaching, and service. Of late, a fourth aspect of academic work has started to emerge and it is one that I just cannot bring myself to stomach. We are all expected to participate in fundraising, and are repeatedly prompted to become more active in this regard. We are all supposed to mingle with alumni and beg them for money, which would go to basic department operations. We are supposed to kiss up to our current students to ensure they have a nice experience and start giving early, and then continue giving, so we can actually make some serious money off of them when they are middle-aged and successful (apparently, research shows that people who start giving early remain donors throughout their lives). I really find it distasteful that we, as faculty, now have to go schmooze left, right, and center to convince people to give us money, even more so when we are effectively trying to manipulate our current students, priming them to become lifelong donors. What's sad is how zealously the local administration has jumped on the bandwagon and some people I know are smart are talking like zombies: how this fundraising is exactly what has to be done and that we are only now seeing the light and how this is the best thing ever and how all this money is going to make everything and everyone awesome. What?!

Upon becoming a professor, it took me a while to process that I would have to support my own research from federal grants and that there would be virtually no safety net provided by the university. But now we have to raise money for basic operations, e.g., to get less-than-ancient equipment for undergrad labs? We are not a start-up, we are an institution of higher learning, where these PhDs called professors are supposed to teach people and do research. Since when does schmoozing with rich alumni fall under the job description? In my field, most people are on the fairly nerdy end of the spectrum; effortlessly loosening the purse strings of donors is not among the skill set my colleagues or I possess.

The decline in state support to this institution, which is the state flagship, is beyond disturbing. Why pretend that you care about having a world-class research university when you clearly don't? You are cutting support, yet forcing us to keep the tuition low, and reducing us to begging for charity. I thought that by working for a public university I would be paid less than in industry, but would be my own boss and have a secure and dignified job, relatively decoupled from corporate America. Silly me.

Chapter 11

Work–Life Balance

Little Pockets of Time

It's just after quittin' time on Friday, most of my brood went swimming with my husband, dinner is in the oven, and I have about 20 minutes before I need to tend to it again. That is 20 minutes of unexpected free time, one of life's most delightful gifts. It's a perfect amount, really — too short to really focus on something technically challenging or dive into serious writing (like a proposal that I am working on), but enough to take care of some small work items, such as editing a student's conference abstract (or two).

These little bits of freedom bring me more joy than the larger blocks of scheduled time for certain activities, simply because they are unexpected. It is similar to hearing a favorite song on the radio — I have no idea when it will happen, so when it does, it really cheers me up. Listening to a downloaded version whenever I want just doesn't have the same uplifting effect.

The Sucky and Awesome of Academia

Even when you have a great job, sometimes work makes you cranky. Here's an off-the-top-of-my-curmudgeonly head list of things that suck about being a professor, as well as those I still realize are great despite my acute grumpiness.

The sucky:

1) It is hard constantly facing criticism and rejection. Even acceptances don't come without criticism and considerable follow-up work. Sure, we are all fighting the good fight for the accuracy of science, so sloppy or incomplete work should not get a pass, but, after what I have seen as an author, reviewer, and associate editor in the past month, I am finding it really, really hard not to start getting disillusioned by the peer review process. There are many people with too much ego and too much time on their hands, ranging from obnoxiously nitpicky to downright malicious.

2) **Nobody ever pats you on the back or tells you "Good job."** Ever. Except perhaps the people whose approval in the professional arena doesn't mean much, like your partner or your parents. The fact that you are supposed to go on forever based on your own convictions and some internal source of energy, without ever expecting to get a little back in the form of praise from colleagues in the professional community is a really tall order. I used to have motivation in spades, but I never expected that I would have to be the sole engine propelling myself and all my group members for the next 40+ years. I praise my students when they do a good job, but for us grown-ups there is no such thing. I

suppose you get an award every now and then, but what's that, a pat on the back every few years? That is a lean affirmation diet.

3) **You are not supposed to complain to anyone, ever**. Sure, colleagues are not friends, but there are not many non-academics who can understand the peculiar stresses of academic life, and even academics from remote fields may have a hard time relating to many of the discipline-specific issues. I can't remember the last time I had a substantive chat with a colleague or collaborator. It's always just small talk or very technical exchanges. No signs of weakness or doubt are to be displayed — loser-talk alert! However, complaining as a vehicle for bragging is totally OK: "I had to work around the clock all week just to write reports for the eight new grants I received last year. And my wallet's too small for my fifties and my diamond shoes are too tight!" But mostly it's just, "I am busy, but of course I am on top of things and everything is just peachy. I am not even tired! I've totally got this." Or maybe I am simply not accustomed to being a grown-up. Nobody wants to hear your problems anywhere, amirite? That's what therapists are for.

Numbers 2 and 3 are kind of the same thing, I guess — isolation and competitiveness.

The awesome:

1) **Being a tenured professor in a physical-science field is a well-paid, secure job, with great benefits** (at least where I am). It enables me to pay for a spacious house, daycare, afterschool care, and summer camps. It allows me to afford 20-ounce lattes with biscotti when I feel particularly naughty.

2) I really, *really* like being my own boss. I am at a major public research university, and the pay in my field is good, although it would be much better at a private university and better still in industry. However, nowhere outside of academia would I get to be my own boss. Also, I don't mind being the boss of others.

3) Teaching undergrads is a lot of fun. Some of my colleagues are afraid of undergrads and avoid teaching lower-level courses whenever possible; in contrast, I really enjoy them. The key is to understand that undergrads just look big, but are really kids inside; they are often completely terrified. Even though I may be teaching something for the umpteenth time, everything is new to them and that makes it fresh for me, too.

4) I love working with my grad students. They are smart and kind, and it is awesome watching them turn into professional scientists. Nothing brings my spirits up like talking science with a student at the whiteboard in my office.

Everyday Superpowers

When people ask me how I do all that I do, I usually answer, "poorly." I think the key to living my life has been a combination of 1) stamina, 2) the ability to embrace imperfection, and 3) figuring out what I really needed, then going for it.

First, I have always had the capacity to do a tremendous amount of work under pressure, and I used to find these bouts of hyper-focus and productivity invigorating. There are only 24 hours in a day, of which normal humans sleep 6–8; I could generate more time for work when necessary by working around the clock, with tremendous amounts of coffee and adrenaline.

Endurance used to be my superpower, but of late I have started to notice that I can't do it as much as I used to. I think I am simply getting too old and worn out. I feel that I need the sleep more than I used to and I definitely work better when rested. Another part of the story is that, as you progress through the academic ranks, your workload never lessens. You just get more and more piled on, but many tasks that are important and urgent are of the "in my heart of hearts, I don't actually care" variety, so it's hard to make myself pull out all the stops and lose more sleep to get it done. Sometimes, I just slack off, really badly.

Second, getting a lot done while also being an involved parent requires embracing imperfection. My house could be cleaner. I could spend time and money decorating. My kids and I could be stylishly dressed. I could also work more, give better talks, submit each paper for publication only when polished to perfection and only to the highest-profile journals. I constantly prioritize and reprioritize, and things that are not high priority get dropped, or postponed, or done sloppily. Then I move on.

Raising kids is not for the faint of heart and not for people who cannot relinquish control, because it's inherently really messy, in every way imaginable. With multiple kids, kid–kid interactions add complications of epic proportions. Going with the flow is really the best way to keep your head above water. Luckily, kids need love, food and shelter, structure and stability, but they don't need overscheduling or micromanaging. From having kids I have learned — or, more accurately, I am still learning — that we actually have remarkably little control over our lives. So I make plans and work hard toward fulfilling them, but make contingency plans for when things go wrong, because they often do, and when they do, it's important to act quickly, make a decision, cut losses if needed, and just keep going.

Third, it is very important to be in touch with what you want. It can actually be very hard to sift through everything that you are supposed to want or be and get to the bottom of what you need, to what is really important. Even if you know what it is, you might feel like you don't have the right to go for it, or that it's not the right time, or that going for it will hurt someone (all of these have happened to me more than once). It helps to take it easy on yourself and allow for imperfection; maybe you don't know what you want today, but will in a few months. Maybe you don't have the guts to go after what you want now, but you might later. I know that I generally always know, deep inside, what I want, but often delay it or don't act on it at all. But being able to understand what you want and allow yourself to have it is critical for happiness.

I think people often assume that there is something wrong with the things that they want and they deny themselves. Sometimes what you want is hard to get or dangerous or imprudent, sometimes it hurts others, but if you are constantly feeling unhappy and tired, but are physically healthy, it's worth asking whether there are things deep down that make you unhappy and that could be changed, and what is keeping you from changing them.

A few years ago, I thought I had completely lost my mojo and my professional future looked rather bleak, as in, "Why am I doing any of this? Everything is stupid." Then I realized I was doing way too much of what I thought was expected of me and too little of what I wanted. So at some point my feeling miserable overcame my anxiety about doing the wrong thing, and that finally gave me the courage to do what I wanted to do all along.

Give yourself permission to go after as many of the things that you really want as you can, without putting anyone in jail or needlessly endangering anyone's life, limb, sanity, or long-term well-being.

Academental Health

I have been reading *A Guide to Rational Living* by Albert Ellis and Robert A. Harper, which I understand to be *the* book on rational emotive behavioral therapy (REBT). I picked it up after my husband had started reading it (yes, we sometimes read the same book in parallel, two bookmarks, whoever gets to it reads it) on the recommendation of my husband's brother, whose high-strung, neurotic personality resembles mine in many ways. If I were to sum up the REBT philosophy about two-thirds of my way into the book, it would be that prolonged negative feelings (e.g., rage, anxiety, depression) stem from one's so-called irrational beliefs, which we unknowingly keep reinforcing but which need to be dispensed with. REBT advocates challenging these deep-seated "awfulizing" beliefs that make everything seem much worse than it is and which are often quite ridiculous when you start to pick them apart, in order to take the power away from them so we can stop feeling stuck or miserable over essentially nonexistent woes. I think most of us could use a bit more positive outlook in our lives. (By the way, I understand cognitive behavioral therapy (CBT) and REBT are closely related.)

The book and the patient cases described therein made me think of all the people I have met through the years, mostly in academia, who have had mental or behavioral health issues. I don't know whether academia is rife with mental health problems or whether it is better or worse than any other industry, but I know I have met quite a few individuals who might have or actually have benefited from some form of therapy.

After completing my bachelor's degree, I taught physics part time at an elite high school for kids gifted in math and science. The students were exceptionally bright and the school was a pressure cooker. Every year, several students would have breakdowns and have to leave.

Shortly after I began grad school in the US, I witnessed a professor undergo a dramatic mental health collapse. The professor was subsequently diagnosed with a psychiatric disorder and has been controlling the condition with medication reasonably well ever since.

Recently, a former visiting scientist sent several cryptic, incoherent emails. Upon exchanging a few emails with his former advisors, it appeared that similar emails were sent to all the scientist's acquaintances. He became manic after too much stress and too little sleep for far too long. I don't know what the future will hold for him.

A colleague from another department left his tenure-track position after only two years. Having spiraled into deep depression, he finally sought and received help, left the job for which he felt poorly suited and found one that seems to make him much happier.

Academics move for their job a lot and are usually very far from a strong support network of close friends and family. The work is stressful, replete with rejection and with few affirmations. In many fields, job prospects are mediocre to bleak, yet personal sacrifices are often great. So people suffer.

Academic Breathlessness

Academic careers are long, averaging 30–40 years. I look at my colleagues who are in their mid-50s, which is supposed to be one's career peak. I see some who are really leaders in their respective fields, but others seem to have … run out of breath. In my totally unscientific observation, there are several tightly interwoven reasons for this academic breathlessness. In a nutshell: we are not in Kansas anymore.

Science moves faster than it used to. What it means to be active and do notable work has changed. How your work correlates with your standing in your local and international environments has changed. Some people have not been able to successfully adapt. It used to be that you could spend your whole career working in a single field and slowly chip away at a big important problem. There used to be more departmental support for students and acceptable group sizes were smaller. The number of papers you needed to publish per unit time in order to be considered active was lower.

Today, there is a great emphasis on external funding. Your department and college gravitas are directly proportional to how much overhead you bring in and how large your group is. What used to be enough for tenure 20 years ago would not be tenurable now. More people do science, there is a greater variety of topics, and individual topics come in and out of fashion much more quickly. (The fact that people talk about fashion in research is a relatively recent development, too.) Unfortunately, one's ability to obtain the ever-important funding depends on one's ability to follow these fast-moving trends. People who are more aggressive by temperament and have a gift for smelling that the change is coming, and then follow (or better yet, lead) these fad shifts do better than others. Also, people who are already well funded and have large groups are better able to quickly adjust — you can always assign a postdoc and three grad students to work on an emerging trend or just your own far-off ideas if you have five postdocs and 25 students, without endangering your baseline productivity.

Someone who's out of breath is not a bad person or a bad scientist, just someone who has been run over by the stampede. They try to engage in the newer, hotter, faster-moving topics, but their baseline expertise is too far removed, the barrier to entry too high. Their field is nowhere near as important now as it was 20 years ago. I am sure they were perfectly tenurable at the time and continued doing what they were doing for a while, but it's no longer enough.

In most STEM fields, there is a tendency these days to hire and tenure people who are much more aggressive than the average of previous crops. There are very driven, forceful people among the mid-to-late career cohort, too, and they seem to remain well funded and relevant in the brave new world of academic science. It pains me to say that I see a number of theorists in the breathless group. It's understandable because they don't make gadgets and funding is quite scarce for the non-gadget-making among us. Also, many theorists are deep-thinking introverts, which, unfortunately, is not necessarily a strength in the new landscape. I feel for the colleagues who are struggling to follow the rules of the new game, owing to ill-suited temperament or expertise, and it probably doesn't get easier with age.

The key is to observe how the game is played and how the most successful people play it, *but then you have to make it your own*.

My proposal-writing rate is such that I have enough money for the size of the group I have, but I have a somewhat lean operation and rely on my own strengths, such as the ability to pick out really smart students, carefully coach each one, and write papers really fast. I have found the optimal group size for me to maintain a high publication rate, while effectively training new students. Each group member has their own project, different from everyone else's, and leaves with a strong publication record. That's how I meet the metrics of publication output as well as remain relevant and nimble (a few smart students plus me, always learning alongside them).

A particular breathless colleague is smart and certainly capable of doing good work. I think he understands how the academic game, version Y2K, is played, but is not implementing the knowledge as he should. He does not have very good students, which correlates with him not being able to pay them, so he has a limited pool and no ability to effectively recruit from the incoming crop. In that case, if I were him, I would do more of the heavy lifting myself. If I really wanted to switch to a new field but could not really rely on my existing students, I would devote several months to learning on my own about what the field cares about and talk to colleagues with pertinent expertise for a reality check. Then I'd think long and hard about what types of open problems I would be uniquely qualified to answer in that field; being on the outside is actually an asset in this case. Instead, he's letting the not-so-great students lead the way and he's not really making an effort to learn what people care about in the field into which he supposedly wants to move. As a result, the work may be totally irrelevant.

I suppose if I were to summarize the Early 21st Century Rules of the Academic Game in STEM for people looking to switch fields, it would be the following: To stay relevant, you have to care (i.e., learn) about what other people care about. Then decide what skills and expertise you uniquely bring to the table and use them to address these open problems, which will bring relevance and eventually funding. For many people, relevance and funding are an end unto themselves, and that's perfectly fine. But, if you are not like that, it's good to know that, once you have relevance and funding, you can also work on your own offbeat stuff, too, and people will actually find it charming (perhaps even visionary!) as opposed to thinking that you are being left behind.

Limits

An important aspect of growing up is realizing you have limits. You might reach different types of limits at different times — for instance, most people realize sooner or later that they will never make it as professional athletes because they are simply not good enough, and never will be, even with lots and lots of practice.

Sometimes the limits are not even hard ones, but rather the limits you choose to impose on yourself, more or less consciously, and they can be a way of asserting what you really want or need.

Being a tenured professor comes with its own challenges. Over the past decade, I have been a member of several large centers, as that seems to be the way funding is increasingly distributed these days. But I really hate the model, as it results in projects that are underfunded and heavily leveraged against individual grants anyway. Yet, every participant's effort in terms of meetings and outreach is just staggering. The centers I have been involved with have been considerably more pain than they are worth.

This year has been the year of considerably increased job satisfaction for me, after a steady decline in motivation. The main reason is that I finally reached my limits in terms of what I can take on the bullshit-work front. I got to the point that I could not find any energy to do my work, and I see now that it is because I have listened too closely to what others have been saying that the modus operandi of a successful academic in my field has to be: collaborations, having your fingers everywhere, participating in big centers; more talk about work instead of working; more silly PowerPoint slides about how we are all organized, integrated, leveraged, and synergized; money, money, money, money, money; meetings and collaborations that would lead to more money for everyone, which would be spent on appeasing higher administration and paying young people to do research that we barely have the time to oversee.

Reaching the point where I was asking, "*Why* exactly would I be doing this for the next 30 years?" forced me to evaluate what it is that would make it worthwhile and why I wanted the job to begin with, which gave me the courage to get rid of some of the shackles of tedious center affiliations and stifling collaborations. I am back to a very lean operation with me and my students, and I am having fun again. I am apparently a very old-fashioned professor, one who will never be a big center director in command of multimillion-dollar budgets, or a powerful administrator. To me, the freedom of tenure means I get to go back to doing what I love — to think, read, write, and advise students with renewed vigor.

Saying No to Invited Talks

The dearth of women invited speakers at conferences is a well-known problem. Some people have said that women, when invited, seem to decline more often than men. If that is true, the question is why. I can't speak for all women, but here are some reasons why I decline these invitations.

When I was a junior faculty member and all such talks counted for a lot on my CV, I accepted nearly all invitations. Invited talks are like getting credit: when you are young and you need it, no one will give it to you; when you are old, established, with a paid-off house and ample savings and no need for credit, everyone bends over backward to give it to you. Same thing with invited talks: nobody gives them to the young'uns, who'd jump at the chance and whose CVs the talks would positively enhance.

Why do I accept talks now that I have tenure and my career is doing fine? I generally go to a conference if: 1) it is one of the two or three conferences that are very specifically in my field (even so,

I prefer one of these over the others, and usually go to that one but send students to the others), 2) it is a closely related field where I usually have something new to learn that benefits my research directly, or 3) I owe it to the organizers (e.g., I declined a talk a couple years ago because of pregnancy, and the organizer is a respected colleague, so this year I will do it even though it's an international trip and it's a pain). Also, I agree to give invited talks at one of the big meetings, such as the American Physical Society March Meeting.

As for lectures, I generally give them at the places where I know someone, or where I want to meet someone. Giving a lecture is usually accompanied by a day or two of nonstop meetings and talking with many faculty and students, and can be quite exhausting. Early on in my career, it was easier to get invited lectures than invited talks at conferences, so I used to jump on every opportunity to give one. Now I do them sparingly and, whenever possible, I try to give multiple talks back to back or to host someone at my university instead.

Why do I decline invited talks, or avoid going to conferences in general? Some reasons are professional, some personal.

Professional reasons. There are a couple of communities where I am well known and respected, and those conferences are generally enjoyable, even if I know the community a little too well and know exactly what everyone else is doing.

But then there are the conferences where I am either unknown or semi-known, but where I could in principle learn new things. That's where sexism rears its ugly head and it has become really tiresome to battle. Perhaps this situation is a little similar to how gay people have to constantly come out to everyone new they meet, over and over again, because everyone's default expectation is that they are straight. (I am in no way trying to downplay how hard this must be; I can only imagine.) My experience at new meetings is that the default expectation, perhaps because I am still a youngish woman, is that I don't have much interesting or important to say. I am presumed incompetent until proven otherwise. In some communities people are more hostile than in others. While I was more junior, I needed the travel, the exposure, and I dutifully endured the task of convincing random, unpleasant male scientists over and over that I in fact knew what I was doing. Sometimes even random junior schmucks consider themselves superior just because they are men. These days I can afford not to do that anymore; if I go to a conference once and don't like the vibe, I won't go again. Also, I don't play all that nice any more with Douchey McDouchersons, which may not make me popular in certain communities. Bottom line, I avoid this type of irritation if I can help it. Life is too short to constantly fight for the approval of random new people.

Last but not least, many invited talks come with few expenses paid. Therefore, unless it's a conference I would attend anyway, or it somehow directly relates to what I work on or would like to work on, I don't go. Most of my declinations this year were due to some combination of general irrelevance to my work and the organizers not covering enough.

Personal/family reasons. My kids have different activities and schedules that require two parents to juggle. One can say that when I am out of town there can be a part-time nanny to help, and that's perfectly valid. But, at this point in my career I can afford to say that I don't care about travel enough to go through the trouble of finding part-time care for these situations. The few families I know who do have part-time drop-off/pickup care often complain that the schedules don't work out and that the care providers they really like cannot make the hours needed. I am comfortable blowing off some travel for increased sanity for myself, my kids, and my husband. When I am gone, they are stressed as things are disrupted, but if I am seldom gone, the disruption is still just a disruption, not the norm.

We have always used daycare centers for childcare for two main reasons: one is that centers take care of backup when the teacher is sick or has time off; the other is that I don't trust myself to choose a good person on my own and daycare centers do a thorough check of all their staff. Now that we have been with a center for a while, we have a wonderful woman who is a teacher there babysitting our kids on occasion, and she even watched our children overnight once. But precisely because she is so great, we do not want to bother her too much and we try to only use her sparingly. If I were on the tenure track now, having to travel quite heavily, I would have no problem leaving my kids with this woman, but hindsight is 20/20. Still, I definitely understand that people may not be comfortable leaving their kids for several days with someone they don't know well.

One important question is whether, by not giving invited talks, I am somehow hurting the young women who come after me. I don't know; perhaps I am. All I know is that I cannot, just because I am a woman, be expected to be responsible for all the young women scientists in my field. If I have to go give invited talks at the expense of my work–life balance so I would be a good role model for aspiring female scientists, then does that mean all stay-at-home-moms have to go back into the workforce so they would be good role models for their daughters who might want to work? Yeah, right.

An academic career is long. The tenure-track sprint comes with many sacrifices, which is fine, but many are such that they cannot be sustained over the marathon that is an entire career. Some people travel a lot and seem to enjoy it. More power to them and to whoever holds down the fort at home — spouses, childcare professionals, magical woodland creatures — in their absence. To me, frequent travel is a nuisance, something I try to minimize for my family's well-being, the health and productivity of my group (they actually prefer me around so they can talk to me), and my own sanity. I am plenty busy just staying put.

The Split Shift

If you are a professor in a STEM field at a research university, you need to work more than the roughly 45 hours per week that kids can typically stay in daycare (or school and afterschool care). Many people, including me, work a split shift: some work gets done during normal business hours, the rest during evenings or weekends. My spouse and kids would not like prolonged periods with me working till 9–10 p.m. (with an occasional past-midnight stint, like yesterday), as I have been doing over the past few weeks because of a looming proposal deadline. Yet, the work has to get done, and there is only so much you can say no to or delegate before you become the self-centered douche on account of whom somebody else now has an insurmountable workload. My kids and spouse definitely prefer me at home in the evenings and on weekends, but occasionally disappearing into the home office to do a few things, over not being around at all. I am far from alone in this type of organization of my time, as I think it's fairly typical for dual-career couples with kids, not just in academia. Academics have more flexibility than most; people in corporate America often have much less control over what hours they work or whether they can disconnect during weekends or evenings.

When you have a job and a family, both of which you love, you burn the candle at both ends. In a way, or perhaps in every way, and on more days than not, *I prefer being stretched too thin to not being stretched enough.* It's good to have a busy life, that's what being youngish and healthy is for. Being relaxed is overrated.

Chapter 12

Women in STEM

Honorary Dudeness

This semester I am again teaching a class with no female students. Lecturing to a 100 percent male audience happens on occasion, typically once every couple of years, and while you'd think it's not that different from teaching a class with one or two women in it, it actually is. It doesn't feel uncomfortable, but it's not entirely comfortable either. I am a middle-aged, female, dog-and-pony show with vector calculus, waving colored markers in front of a whole sea of mostly half-asleep young dudes. My general feelings toward students are warm and motherly — mostly, I realize they are just oversize kids. But the whole experience is ever so slightly weirder with zero female students in the classroom than with at least a few.

Another interesting thing is the relationship that I end up having with the occasional young woman in my class. Either they really like me and we develop a nice connection, or they are squarely at the "this professor sucks" end of the spectrum. Unfortunately, I think that it's common for the women in the fields where they are underrepresented to develop a relationship with their female professors that is at one of these extremes, and keeping other women at arm's length or looking down upon them is actually the more common variant. I know that when you are a young woman in a field dominated by young men and you are competent and confident, you can often seemingly blend in by becoming an Honorary Dude (HD). I spent much of my youth in this mode, cherishing my HD status, because I was smart and meritorious and not like those *other* women. So I can see that competent young women often do come with their own small group of dude friends (who are usually either comparably or less competent than she is) with whom they work and study. I have yet to see two young women in the same circle/study group in any of my classes — it's like no one wants to work with girls, not even other girls, and certainly not the HDs who are "smart and cool, not like *other* girls."

It's a stereotype that women are often weird to other women, the "mean girls" syndrome and all that. Geeky women and their relationship to other geeky women appear to be no exception. What I know is that it took me a long time, which I presume entails growing up, to understand that being an HD is bullshit, that I am a girl/woman, and that no one ever forgets that for one second regardless of how much we all pretend. I also realized that other women really don't need me to crap on their parade and that I should instead help them if I can. Unless another woman has really done something bad to me, I should get over myself and whatever insecurities I have and not demonize her for being successful or having different priorities than me. I am now that woman of whom I used to make fun, who counts the female speakers at conferences and female participants on grant-review panels and female interviewees during faculty searches, and who makes a stink if there are too few or none. Why? Because I grew up and took off my HD badge and realized how disheartening it is to see to what degree my male colleagues — even the "good guys" — really believe that 100 percent men is the norm, and that any women present are really either veritable superstars (even if most men are far from it) or are believed to be a token used to satisfy some political-correctness requirement. This pisses me off, and it's exhausting, but unless I bring it up nobody else does.

We often talk about female students needing female role models and mentors, but I think we need to be aware that we can't a priori count on a female student establishing good rapport with a female teacher. Maybe that female teacher being lame or fat or having an accent or being a minute late to class or however else unworthy of the female student's admiration will actually do less to retain that student than the all-male professorial cast that the young woman expects. For young women, wearing the HD badge and placing even female instructors with all the *other, unworthy* women may well be a necessary survival adaptation. I am established and fairly secure in who and where I am, and I am also older, so I have the luxury of consciously dismantling my HD status among my colleagues or my male students, because I know the status is fake and it hurts other women. So as easy as it would be to continue wearing my HD badge, I keep electing to wear the potentially lame female-professor one instead, and I keep trying to be nicer, more open, and more helpful to other women than even my gut tells me to be, in spite of some young (or not so young) women looking down on me, as they think they know better or that I am weak or silly or matronly for being all female. But the benefit has been that I have also managed to establish better, deeper connections with other women than I have generally had in the past, and I have hopefully become more attuned to and more helpful with the struggles that women in STEM face.

If you are a young woman in STEM, ask yourself how you view your scientific elders. Do you have different, perhaps unreasonable expectations of your female instructors? Are there some female professors you just don't like without being able to point out what it is that you dislike? Do you feel the same way toward your male instructors? What about your peers — are there other girls/young women with whom you study? Ask yourself if you judge your female peers more harshly because they are girls.

Sisterhood

There are quite a few efforts at my university to oversee the well-being of female students and faculty. I am familiar with many, perhaps most, of the programs aimed at women faculty, and I find the vast majority of them to be pretty pointless.

The main issue I have with all the efforts aimed at women faculty, especially with peer-mentoring programs, is that you can't just put two women together and expect they will magically form a nurturing relationship. It doesn't work like that: women, just like real people, can like or dislike someone, even another woman. Shocker, I know. Women do not walk around with an "open for sharing and commiseration, with a possibility of a lifelong friendship" sign on their foreheads. Some women are introverted. Some are jerks. Some just happen not to like you and don't want to have anything to do with you, because reasons (as my preteen would say). If you are lucky, you will find some who are wonderful people and who will also want to get to know you. Mostly, women academics are very busy people, laser focused on their work and their families. They have limited time and energy, and usually aren't willing to devote much of either to random pairings with other women that lead to fleeting, superficial relationships.

When there are very few women in a department or another academic unit, they are often forced to stick together just because they are women, despite their personal incompatibilities. I have certainly heard stories of times not that long ago when you could count all women in my college on the fingers of one hand, so it was critical to create programs that would help these women find and support one another. But, as the number of women increased, the need to huddle together for warmth was no longer dire, so these top-down, programmatic connections started losing relevance.

When women are numerous enough and feel comfortable enough in their academic units to shun women-centered programs and gatherings, this appears to be a good thing. But does it really mean that women are no longer complete aliens in their disciplines, that they can afford not to connect with one another unless there is a compelling personal reason to do so? Or does it mean that women forget all too readily that it is foolish not to remain vigilant about women's position in the workplace, that it is plain selfish not to extend a helping hand to new women in the misguided belief that things are all better now and that they will be fine just by being their individual selves?

Goofy

I often teach undergrads because I seem to be very effective at it — students like me and they leave my classes well prepared for the follow-on courses, the department is aware of it, and I don't mind. Undergrads seem to be quite responsive to my general goofiness and puns, perhaps because they are so young and also because the silliness adds some levity to all the math that I routinely shove down their throats.

Teaching undergrads so often means that this is now really my modus operandi, and the grown-up, bespectacled dudes who are my colleagues are totally unamused by it. I feel I am considerably more goofy when giving talks than the average talk-giving scientist in my general area. This worries me somewhat, because I am a non-bespectacled, non-ancient, long-haired woman (see figure), so I am sure I am, at baseline, not considered as competent as a similarly experienced dude. But I can't turn it off now! I see a crowd and I put on a show! Everyone is engaged and smiling, presumably because people love clowns, or perhaps they feel sorry for me. But nobody is asleep. Still, I wonder how much it's hurting my chances of getting elected a fellow of a professional society or getting into the National Academies.

The poor lady on the left is probably still too young and pretty to be taken 100 percent seriously, despite the impeccable appearance exuding scientific respectability. My avatar is much younger and cuter than I am.

SERIOUS FEMALE SCIENTIST

MOI

XYKADEMOZ '14

Sometimes, it gets to me, being among dudes all the time and being so visibly different, in appearance and demeanor, both from them and from the occasional woman scientist who looks and acts as expected. I love doing science and teaching. But being a female scientist and a female professor can sure be exhausting.

Women sans Babies Q&A

These are my answers to non-motherhood-related questions about being a woman in academia posed during a "blog carnival," where several bloggers answered questions compiled by the blog-carnival host.

1. How do you command the attention, and respect, of men in academic settings (e.g., classrooms, conferences, or faculty meetings)?

I am going to assume here that the question means, "I am technically very competent, but do not feel I command adequate respect. How do I remedy that?" You have to take cues from the guys. Even as young students, when guys think they know the answer to a question they just blurt it out (I sometimes wish they wouldn't). This extends into their professional years. You have to get over the fear of being wrong and simply speak up. The fear does eventually go away. A good exercise is to give yourself the following task: You have to come up with one nontrivial question for each talk you hear at a conference. And then go ahead and ask it. Pretty soon you will be one of the most feared and revered members of any audience!

I am in one of the fields with the most dramatic underrepresentation of women, so the rules of the game are entirely masculine. One of the important differences between men and women (on average, of course) is that women often feel they need external validation, someone to pat them on the back and say, "Good job!" when they are feeling down. I used to be quite unhappy because these compliments were not forthcoming as often as my ego needed them, so I thought I was no good. That was not true — while everyone likes praise, I have found that external affirmation is much less important for an average guy's sense of self-worth than a woman's, so men simply don't volunteer praise easily. So recalibrate. I have learned not to expect pats on the back and to simply rely on what I think is best. And pats on the back do come, but infrequently and indirectly and quite unexpectedly. Sort of like hugs between manly men.

Moreover, use all the nonverbal tricks in the book to communicate that you have gravitas. Wear heels if you need to feel taller, wear clothes that make you feel strong and confident (anything in black makes me feel awesome), stand up straight and speak loudly, make eye contact. If you happen to be tall and/or have a strong voice, be grateful and use these qualities!

2. How should women dealing with a two-body problem handle assumptions that their career is secondary to their partner's?

If stupid questions like these are asked in an inconsequential context (e.g., a random person chatting you up at a party) try to be matter-of-fact and set them straight ("Actually, my significant other is flexible in career choice and will follow me to my position"). The person will usually be embarrassed enough even if you don't go on to tear them a new one for assuming that your gender automatically makes you inferior in ambition or employability.

But, if it's the issue of hunting for jobs, make sure everyone who is important (e.g., all your letter writers and close senior colleagues) knows *exactly* how serious your career plans are. There must be no ambiguity.

3. What would you like to see from tenure-track and not-yet-tenure-track menfolk? How can they pitch in?

When we complain of sexist treatment, shut up and listen with an open mind. Don't be on the defensive — most of us actually don't hate men, quite the contrary. We are just exhausted.

Try to view us as you would your male colleagues and competitors. Try to be honest with yourself about how often, unwillingly, you may think, "She got this because she is a woman" out of pure jealousy. If you catch yourself thinking that a woman is not deserving, ask yourself whether you would think the same of a guy with the same record. I am a woman and I have caught myself valuing a paper less after having found out that the main author was a woman — it was quite a sobering experience. So try to be honest about your biases and work to counteract them.

Speak up for your female lab mates and colleagues. Try to learn what career building is like for us; you will see a path akin to death by a thousand paper cuts. Listen and be empathetic. And then help us fight by putting in good words for us wherever you can. Workplaces that are friendly to women are friendly to all people who strive to have a balance between professional and personal lives.

4. How do you deal with insinuations that you were only chosen for a position/award/etc. because of affirmative action?

As in the answer to question 2: Stupid and/or malicious questions are best deflected with matter-of-fact calmness. "My record is very strong, so I have no doubt I would have been selected even if I were a guy." I think everyone deserves the benefit of a good deflection and a chance to blush and change topics. If they don't take it, i.e., if the person keeps at it, by all means bite their head off. Call them out for being a jealous insecure [insert favorite expletive].

There are situations in which your gender may really have played a positive role. My recommendation is to say, "Thanks!" These breaks are so few and far between that you should not be ashamed or guilty that one happened to fall in your lap. Among a group of equally meritorious peers, people will take any advantage to get ahead — pedigree, network, charm. If for once your gender gets you ahead, great!

5. Are there any suggestions about how to look professorial as a young (and young-looking and smallish) tenure-track faculty? For those of us who like things like pink, skirts, baking, sewing, knitting, heels, makeup, and other things girlie, how important is it to not do /wear/talk about these things lest we be seen as fluffy girls who can't do Science?

These seem like two facets of the question, "I look and act too much like a young woman, how do I make sure it doesn't hurt me professionally?"

"Looking like a professor" means being a white dude with glasses and crazy hair, so that's really hard to pull off for any woman without, at a minimum, gender reassignment surgery. So don't worry about looking like a stereotypical professor. Just look like you and kick ass. I know a number of women, especially from Italy, France, and Spain, who are petite, very feminine, and dress really well. They are also phenomenal scientists and I don't think anyone is taking their looks as a signature of a feeble mind. I am sure you can talk about baking or knitting if you want to, although I don't think I have heard any of them discuss any particular hobbies in a professional setting.

Once your professional record (papers, citations, funding, awards) starts speaking for itself, it is absolutely irrelevant how you look. I know an American-born female professor who's probably no taller than 5' 1" and looks about 12 years old, dresses very casually, and wears no makeup. However, her list of papers, grants, and awards is so impressive that she certainly doesn't have to prove anything to anyone through the way she looks.

Now, what to do until you establish a track record? *Fake it till you make it.* Wear whatever you want and don't worry what anyone else thinks. Or at least tell yourself that you don't care and tell anyone who asks or comments about your appearance that you don't care and that he/she shouldn't either. Young women overwhelmingly suffer from insecurities — that's why faking it is key. Pretend you are confident so doors will open for you; once you have a track record, confidence will naturally come, so you won't have to fake it so much.

As for women professors: I would say wear whatever makes you comfortable, because being uncomfortable shows. Make sure your clothes fit well. That's especially important for women who don't have an ideal physique (most of us no longer do as we age, even if we once did). Also, whatever your clothing style, once you are a professor you can afford higher-end clothes, so go shopping. Get the more expensive version of whatever items you like to wear (this also helps with making sure they fit well). Well-fitting, good-quality clothes, irrespective of style, will make you feel and look like you are comfortable with yourself and in control.

6. What can we do when other women deny there are problems being a woman in science?

When I read this question, I asked myself when was the last time anyone in real life (except my husband and perhaps a close personal friend or relative) actually took my concern to heart when I complained that I suspected someone had slighted me professionally because I'm a woman. The answer is — I cannot remember. It's been a really long time since I complained to anyone from my professional circle in this fashion, not because slights don't happen, but because I have found that colleagues (male and female) really don't want to engage in this type of "what if."

The problem with discrimination against women is that *any one incident happening to any one woman can have an alternative explanation.* That's enough to make you really doubt your qualities and your sanity. Your paper or grant got trashed while the reviewer reveled in writing "she" and "her"? Well, maybe the paper/grant was just really crappy. You are requested to do way more service than your male counterparts? Well, I am sure that's because they really appreciate your contribution to the department, since you are so good at it. You got passed up for a fellowship/scholarship/promotion? Well, maybe that other (white, male) candidate really was better qualified.

Since any one incident can have an alternative explanation, if you suspect gender bias and go to a colleague (male or female) for support, don't be surprised if they don't jump to agree with you or comfort you. Many of them will think (even if they are not saying it) that *you* are not good enough, that you are simply not passing muster. Don't be surprised by such thinking — academic science is extremely competitive and people have huge egos. Showing doubt and insecurity, in my experience, usually does not fall on receptive ears. Pats on the back are very hard to come by, so you had better get used to living without them.

However, *bias against women is well documented and real because many, many women have the exact same ambiguous, unpleasant experiences happening to them.* That is why it doesn't matter what any one naysayer says in response to any one or a host of your anecdotes. It is a fact that over the course of your career you will most likely get some (or quite a bit of?) friction under your professional wheels because you are a woman. Life is definitely too short to try to convert naysayers. If you suspect that someone is biased against you professionally, don't waste your time going around looking for validation; assume they are indeed biased and try to minimize their influence on your career. (I am talking about unconscious bias and the virtually imperceptible inequalities it creates; egregious violations of your rights to a safe work environment or sexual harassment should always be reported.) Focus on surrounding yourself with supportive people of both genders, and keep looking and going ahead.

7. It seems that women often don't have as strong professional networks as men — the kind that gets built over shared interests (sports or drinking). People seem to gravitate toward others like them. What specific advice do you have for establishing and maintaining a network with men as well as other women?

I am in a very macho field, so my network consists almost exclusively of men. I eat and drink everything, and I don't mind going to sports bars or any other kind of bar/restaurant. I don't follow sports or politics closely so I usually don't discuss them, but there is usually plenty of chatter about conferences, people we all know, developments in the field, travel, university or company politics, families, so there are many topics where I can participate in the conversation. Most men in my field are moderate drinkers and family men, and really aren't all that wild or all that scintillating as dinner conversationalists. I also steer the conversation toward talking shop when I need to, and it is usually well received. I guess I am old enough that networking gets easier, as we are all getting old and boring — dinner, one drink, then back to the room to sleep or work.

When I was a grad student, my male grad student brethren were a bit wilder in terms of drinking and ogling women, but I can hold my liquor and have a fairly high threshold for comments about the racks of random girls passing by, so it wasn't a big deal. Even then, most conversations were about sports, current politics, movies, travel, or our advisors. I guess we were pretty boring then, too.

Go out with people you meet at conferences and don't think about it too much. You can nurse your Coke or vodka-tonic all night, most people don't care. Take part in the conversation when you can, otherwise listen or chill and people-watch. If you are comfortable, people will be comfortable around you. I routinely go out to dinner with groups of men and no other women. Long ago I was very uncomfortable; now I don't even notice. I remember a recent grant program review (it's like a workshop), where I ended up renting a minivan at the airport because the rental car company was out of compacts and midsize sedans; it turned out well, as I could drive a whole bunch of us (me and six middle-aged men) out of town to a steak house, so we didn't have to take multiple cars. And none of them even complained that a woman was driving!

What Impostor Syndrome Is About for Women in STEM

When you bring up the issue that affirmation in science is rare and scientists don't really praise each other, you will receive comments in all the usual macho veins of "Toughen up!" or "Who cares what anyone else thinks?" or "Maybe you are not that good anyway." On one particular occasion, in a comment section of a blog far, far away, one male commenter said, "[I]f you need external reinforcement to keep you going, science definitely isn't the career for you," while another chimed in, "If you are not receiving praise, it might not be the system. It might be that you just don't deserve any praise."

What was amazing is that it took over two dozen comments before someone brought up, "It's not the system, it's that you suck." Because the person craving affirmation would never ever in a million years think of this mind-bending option themselves.

Now imagine that you are a woman in a male-dominated discipline (and mine is as male-dominated as they come). Every class in your undergrad and grad school, every conference room, and every classroom in which you teach as a faculty member is a dude-a-palooza.

You constantly work against the background noise of, "You don't belong here. You should not be doing this. This is not a place for you." There is a tremendous overhead in terms of sheer energy, motivation, and perseverance that one has to put in just to get up in the morning to do the work. Trust me, women in male-dominated disciplines don't have the issue of lack of motivation; just the fact that they are there and haven't fled is a testament to their tenacity, which, if we could somehow measure it, we would find few men could rival. But much of it must continuously be used on fighting this negative background, which men really don't have to do. Men are not constantly receiving messages that they are constitutionally unable or unworthy to do their work, nor are they assumed incompetent until proven otherwise. For men, competence is assumed.

Perhaps, to a dude, thinking, "It might be that I just don't deserve any praise" sounds like a revolutionary leap in introspection. To a woman, this is something we constantly ask ourselves. Then we teach ourselves how to block it, how not to ask that question constantly, lest we drive ourselves insane. Honestly, on many days I don't go on because I believe in myself or my work; I go on in spite of overwhelming doubts, because I have a job to do, students to work with, and obligations to federal funding agencies.

So I quietly chuckle whenever I hear, "If you are doubtful, you are not tough enough; science is not for you" or "Well, maybe you are just not good enough," as they are such predictable responses; they likely come from people who never really had deep self-doubts about doing science or doing it well. But a woman in a male-dominated field internalizes these sentiments, as they are part of the baseline feedback she constantly gets from her scientific community. A woman receives this information *regardless of how good she objectively is,* which is why this is so frustrating — it is very hard to decipher whether it is really merit (or lack thereof) or just more of the *"You are other, we don't trust you know anything, maybe you should just go away."* Remembering that women are, at least on average and definitely to a degree much greater than men, socialized to be people-pleasers, you can see how this combination of upbringing with a chilly climate in the professional arena requires enormous amounts of energy to just remain there and keep doing your job.

Next time a female colleague, a woman scientist, complains that she feels undervalued and underappreciated, please don't start with knee-jerk responses — "Toughen up!" and "Maybe you don't deserve praise!" *You know you think these things even if you don't say them out loud.* Assume, for a change, that she is plenty tough and that she really deserves the praise; it's just that she is really, *really* exhausted from doing science while pushing uphill that Sisyphean rock of gender bias, day after day. Offer to buy her a caffeinated beverage and praise her for the good work she does.

Or simply talk science with her like she's an equal, not an impostor.

Sexist Logorrhea

Not that long ago, a septuagenarian Nobel laureate blurted out that women were are a distraction in the lab and cried a lot, then called for gender-segregated labs. The Internet erupted.[2]

---

[2] For a summary of the Tim Hunt affair, see for instance Phil Plait's article "Which Hunt?" at Slate.com (accessed May 2, 2016), slate.com/blogs/bad_astronomy/2015/07/01/tim_hunt_nobel_laureate_s_comments_about_girls_and_science.html.

Whatever. I am actually relieved every time something like this happens. I am relieved that occasionally someone is actually stupid enough to say out loud what many think and act according to anyway.

Over the past several years, I have been a witness to pretty serious discrimination of other women by people considerably younger than the man above. These men would fight you to the death if you even hinted that they are sexist, because of course they don't think they are; yet, their actions speak differently.

- "We have enough women," said in earnest by a colleague in a faculty meeting discussing hiring. Women make up less than 20 percent of faculty.

- "L is not a real candidate," said by a colleague about a female candidate. The colleague and I were on the recruitment committee together, I know we ranked all candidates, top 20 were all stellar, L was ranked third, and we interviewed five. She was not a diversity candidate; she was a highly qualified candidate who also happens to be female.

- A few years back, some colleagues and I went through serious diversity training in preparation for serving on the faculty-recruitment committee. I thought the training was illuminating. That's where I first found out about how women are expected to be communal and men agentic, and how women are penalized if they are perceived to be insufficiently communal. I saw the examples of recommendation letters and the difference in the language people use for men and women, how letters for women always veer toward too personal, with comparatively less focus on achievement, excellence, and competence, and with different adjectives used for women and men. The male colleagues went through the motions and, when it was all done, said it was all pointless bullshit and a waste of time. We all saw those letters; they completely shook my world, but apparently did nothing for my male colleagues. You truly can lead a horse to water, but you cannot make it drink.

- At the university level, we reviewed three candidates from the same general field (different subfields) coming up for tenure. If you just looked at the number of publications and quality of journals where they appeared, the number of citations, the number of grants, the woman was the best of the lot. But if you looked at external evaluation letters, you'd be appalled by the language. According to the letters, the two men were superstars in the making (not made yet, with writers bending over backward to attribute lack of citations to the fact that the candidate is a visionary), while the woman's achievements were downplayed, with statements to the effect that she must have come up with some of her most heavily cited findings by accident! It was disgusting. I'd read about these instances happening, but it was blatant and real and clear as day. These letters then led to the committee dissecting the woman's record with a scalpel and a fair bit of skepticism; everything worthwhile she did had to be qualified, while the men were fine just on potential and the letters. (You bet I was vocal about it.)

- Being a member of the program committee for a conference in my field, it routinely happens that there are no women suggested for invited talks unless I suggest some. It's amazing how I can think of three or four women easily, and the other 15 dudes together cannot think of a single one.

That is not to say that there aren't men who really and truly are the champions of women. They exist (thank you, guys!), but are definitely a minority. For instance, I have the good fortune that some of my departmental colleagues, including the chair, are genuinely supportive of women and really put their money where their mouth is: they advise female students and actively support female colleagues. However, I would say that less than 20 percent of men in my department truly believe a diverse workplace is a better place for everyone. The rest make allowances for exceptional specific women ("Of course, you are awesome! You are much better than other women!"), but do not see why there is a need for diversity; science is fine just the way it is! They consider all our "hysteria" about women in science to be tiresome political bullshit that has to be catered to when writing about broader impacts in NSF proposals. They will often say things such as "We hire the best candidate, not an affirmative-action candidate!" To everyone who ever said that I want to say the following: It sounds like you have no clue how it is to objectively evaluate candidates for anything very competitive. There are always many highly qualified candidates, any one of them would be a good choice. Now the question is how to pick one or some other small number from among these uniformly excellent men and women. I am disgusted to see that people think all of these few spots belong (!) to "real candidates," i.e., men. The fact that a woman is just as good as any of them still does not make her a real candidate in the eyes of some, even fairly junior colleagues with professional wives and daughters.

Many men in the physical sciences, even among those who think very highly of their own enlightenment, don't really think that science *needs* more diversity, but rather that it's simply something women want and are very loud and annoying about, and should thus be accommodated on occasion to stop the whining (or to snatch the rarely seen unicorn-female-superstar-real-candidate). They consider all efforts to promote women as a nuisance that gets in the way of doing science as they are used to. My European colleagues can be a special brand of offender here, as they often see (and speak of) the quest for promotion of women as an American problem and not something relevant to where they live and work (this from a colleague who works on a large team of about 50, with a single woman, who is a student). It is very hard to change people's minds when they think they are blind to sexism and that all they see is merit. Trying to convince them that much of the merit is really in the eye of the beholder would be positively quixotic.

So I don't understand the outrage that a sexist male scientist suffers from the foot-in-mouth disease. Really, it's not a surprise. It's just how things are.

Superlative Fatigue

Superlative fatigue — a condition that emerges after writing too many letters of recommendation or award nominations within a short period. It stems from the inability of the human brain to use, in earnest, more than a limited number of superlatives per unit time without wanting to vomit or use more realistic adjectives. The condition is particularly severe in North America, specifically in the United States, where discussing someone's mere excellence in academic pursuits is woefully inadequate, and all manner of Red Sea parting, water-to-wine turning, and water-on-foot traversing must be described instead. There is evidence that the residents of Lake Wobegon may be immune to superlative fatigue.

It has been shown that some letter writers in the STEM fields (usually, but not exclusively, men) can successfully stave off superlative fatigue by writing a letter for a female student or colleague. Similar to how the aroma of coffee beans resets one's sense of smell after sampling perfumes, composing a letter on behalf of a woman can completely reset the letter writer's superlative counter, so the next real letter, for a man, can again employ the full force of superhuman-worthy embellishments. This effect apparently arises from the total absence of necessity to ever use superlatives when describing the professional accomplishments of women, because everyone knows that it's better to use the more appropriate womanly qualifiers, such as "warm," "collegial," "hard-working," or sometimes "difficult," "insecure," and "accidentally stumbled upon her main finding."

Survival Tips for Young Women in STEM

(Originally appeared in Inside Higher Ed)

Being a young woman in a field dominated by men is, at the very least, challenging. Science, technology, engineering, and math (STEM) are such fields. There are few female role models. There are few female peers, so women feel isolated. Similar to other underrepresented minorities, women face enhanced professional expectations (a woman must do twice as much to get half the recognition) in order to successfully combat the perception of intellectual inferiority. There are many stereotypes about a woman's priorities or career plans ("Of course you want babies and a family," even though you say you don't, or "Since you have children, you are certainly not working as hard as you should," or "You will certainly follow your husband for his job"). There is a large body of literature about the challenges of women in science and engineering: a quick Google search will reveal a number of articles, blogs, and forums that the reader is encouraged to explore. I will not argue whether or not women face obstacles in STEM careers. They do.

Instead, I am going to try and give some practical tips on how to navigate what I feel is a typical STEM graduate experience for a woman, largely based on my own experiences. As a graduate student in a physical-science discipline notorious for its low representation of women, I was often the only woman in my graduate classes. Even when I wasn't alone, women never exceeded 10–15 percent of the class, and this percentage remains true for most graduate programs in my discipline. What I write here is by all means not exhaustive; it resembles what I would say to a female student who would come to my office for advice.

While I consider my experiences to be fairly typical, they are not universal; for example, my perspective is that of a white woman, and young women of color often face many additional challenges that I don't address here. Luckily, I believe that a typical experience no longer entails sexual harassment (although there are still terribly unfortunate exceptions), but rather a palette of phenomena that stem from the peers' or PhD advisor's often unconscious biases. Over time, small obstacles to a young woman's professional development can accumulate into a marked disadvantage on the job market, not to mention a permanent scar to the woman's perception of her own worth as a scientist and a person.

Support from female faculty. Young women in STEM are often referred to the few women faculty in their departments for guidance. However, they may find that women faculty have little time to spare and may appear unwilling to engage in a mentoring relationship. It is important not to take rejection personally. For instance, many female professors on the tenure track have small children and a developing research program — both requiring tremendous energy and time. Also, just because a woman is a professor, that does not mean that she is no longer facing biases in her own career — she is often isolated from other women, faces enhanced expectations and preconceived notions from peers, and has to work extremely hard to gain adequate recognition. Therefore, if a junior female faculty is not responsive to your inquiries, don't take it personally, as she probably has a lot on her plate.

I find that the more senior, tenured female faculty are more responsive to inquiries by female students for informal or formal mentorship on how academia works. Tenured professors are more established in their careers and likely have older children, so they might be more willing and able to invest time into helping other women up the academic ladder. But, even so, some tenured women don't see it as a big priority or may be too busy, so if you are having a hard time finding a female mentor in your department, explore other opportunities to find female mentors (see below).

Connect with other women in STEM. It may seem impossible to make friends with other female graduate students when there are virtually none around. However, most professional organizations in STEM disciplines have a designated section to help broaden the participation of women and their career advancement.

Two large interdisciplinary organizations, the Association for Women in Science and the Society of Women Engineers, offer excellent opportunities for mentorship and networking. You may also be interested in the National Academy of Engineering's Engineer Girl, which reaches out to women as well as girls.

Some disciplinary associations include: Association for Women Geoscientists, Earth Science Women's Network, Women in Agronomy, Crops, Soils, and Environmental Sciences, ACS Women Chemists Committee, Women in Biology, Women in Biomedical Careers, Association for Women in Mathematics, ACM's Women in Computing, Women in Physics, AAS Committee on the Status of Women in Astronomy, Women in Aerospace, IEEE Women in Engineering.

Consider joining a local chapter of one or more of these organizations and volunteering. Chances are you will meet many young women such as yourself and also some senior, more established women, who are truly interested in mentoring younger women.

Fight impostor syndrome. Often, young women in academia feel they don't belong in their graduate programs. This is a manifestation of the well-known impostor syndrome, exacerbated in women in STEM because there are so few other women around and so few senior women. The woman can wonder whether she really belongs in the lab. These insecurities are often only deepened by the vibes the woman receives from those around her — their biases against, or simple discomfort due to the presence of a woman. The best way to fight the impostor syndrome is to tell yourself that everyone — everyone! — feels it, even bigwig famous professors. You are not the only one feeling like a fraud, as you will find out once you establish trust and start talking more openly with the people around you.

So don't worry whether you belong. If you are successful in your coursework, if you enjoy your research (for the most part — science has plenty of frustrating moments!) and feel that you are good at it, you most certainly belong in science.

Let stupid remarks slide. Often, people say insensitive things not because they mean to belittle, but because they are themselves insensitive, ignorant, or socially awkward. It helps if you can learn to let the small stuff, especially blunders, slide off your back. I don't mean keeping quiet when things are clearly meant to hurt or offend — by all means speak up. But stupid remarks are sometimes just that: stupid. Learning to distinguish between these two types of remarks can save you plenty of annoyance. For instance, if you have a lab mate who is friendly and supportive of you but occasionally says something that stereotypes you or other women, this person is likely talking from his own biases of which he may not even be aware. Call him on his remarks and explain why they bother you or would bother another woman, but don't give up on your lab mate entirely. Men, especially very young ones, are often unaware of their biases or how some things they say affect women; at the same time, most really don't want to be or to appear sexist and will likely take your comments to heart. Chances are that your male lab peers will be some of your most fervent supporters throughout your career.

Actions speak louder than words. It is generally a good idea to view a person's actions together with what comes out of their mouth. For instance, a senior male member of my PhD committee was very supportive of me in all aspects of my professional career. He also happened to have a bit of a potty mouth and enjoyed somewhat inappropriate jokes of all sorts. It took me a while to realize he simply likes to shock people (women and men) and that in reality he was a supportive and caring mentor.

In contrast, there are many people who have mastered the art of political correctness and are very careful about avoiding verbal blunders. However, they still act according to their sexist or otherwise biased convictions (such as look down on female students, oppose the hiring of female faculty or accommodation of family leave policies). These people are who you should be on the lookout for. Just because a prospective PhD advisor is a smooth talker does not mean that he or she will be supportive or caring of you (or any other student). Before committing to anyone's lab, make sure you talk to other students about how they feel, how the professor treats women and people who are underrepresented minorities, and where the professor's former students are currently employed.

Find support wherever you can. A number of successful women scientists and engineers had supportive male mentors and colleagues. The numbers of men and women in many STEM fields are such that you are exceedingly likely to be advised by a man through much, if not all, of your career. There are many wonderful male professors who are very supportive of women. There are also many wonderful young men, currently your peer graduate students, who will become future professors and will benefit from having smart female peers in graduate school, and from being nudged — gently or a little less so — to grasp what a female scientist's experience is really like.

Try not to depend on women alone for companionship or support. If we are to make STEM labs more equitable, both men and women have to realize it isn't so yet, and both have to work toward removal of bias (to women as well as other underrepresented minorities).

Seek help. In the horribly unfortunate case that you are a young woman facing sexual harassment, please seek external help immediately. If you are feeling very uncomfortable at your place of work or study because of interactions with your peers or your advisor, if anyone is making unwelcome remarks or overtures which you cannot stop, or if someone is making your professional advancement contingent on romantic or sexual involvement, know that these are gross violations of your rights and you ought to talk to someone outside of the lab about the best course of action (such as removing yourself from the situation and penalizing the perpetrator). Many universities have an employee assistance office where you can see a counselor; alternatively you can contact your department administration or the college or university human resources, who will point you to the channels for filing complaints and getting counseling. Getting help and feeling safe again are much more important than any immediate career concerns you may have.

Be a mentor yourself. As you advance through your graduate program (hopefully never knowing harassment) you will become more confident in your command of how things work in graduate school and in your technical specialty. But don't forget the feelings of isolation and doubt, and reach out to new students — of any gender, ethnicity, ability, or sexual orientation — to help them feel welcome and appreciated in the lab. Also, as you progress through your career, many of the issues may resurface, as you have to prove yourself all over again to new colleagues. Staying connected to your professional association, nurturing a network of supportive peers and professional elders, and helping develop a new cohort of enthusiastic scientists are the best ways to ensure long-term satisfaction with your career.

THE DOUBLE BIND

1. HOW A WOMAN ENVISIONS HER CAREER TRAJECTORY

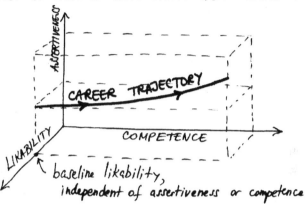

baseline likability, independent of assertiveness or competence

2. HOW THE WORLD SEES WOMEN'S CAREER TRAJECTORIES

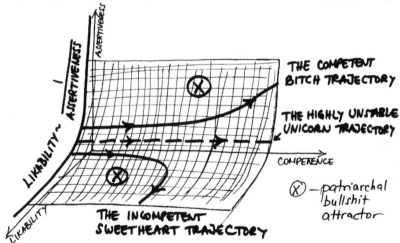

THE COMPETENT BITCH TRAJECTORY

THE HIGHLY UNSTABLE UNICORN TRAJECTORY

Ⓧ — patriarchal bullshit attractor

THE INCOMPETENT SWEETHEART TRAJECTORY

Working-Mom Haiku

I suck to work with
Meetings canceled last minute
because of sick kid

Even in summer
seeing doctor biweekly
like fuckin' clockwork

***

Talk invitations
fill me with dread, for ahead
incessant pumping

Husband gets frazzled
Kids fall sick, violently
Show that mom is missed

***

To quit breastfeeding
was my plan. Looking forward
to caffeine, oh joy!

Silly, making plans ...

Baby can't have milk or soy

Will breastfeed till death

***

Vacation, with kids

Mom and dad totally pooped

Back to work, can't wait

Does Anyone Else Care about Your Work–Life Balance?

No. No one but you, and hopefully your significant other.

There is never a scarcity of conversation about work-life balance on the web, especially for working mothers. There is no shortage of opinion regarding whether it is ethical enough or feminist enough for highly educated women to work part time or drop their careers altogether — some people believe that educated women owe it to society or other women or future generations of boys and girls to keep working; other people believe that women owe nothing to anyone except themselves and their families, and are perfectly within their rights to stay home with their kids and thereby find fulfillment. Whatever your take on these issues, this essay is *not* about them.

No one with whom I am in regular contact in real life gives a rat's ass about my work–life balance: whether I have any, whether I would like to have a different one, whether I face any hardship in achieving any semblance thereof. Everyone in this glorious society is too busy, and presumably too exhausted and overstretched, to think about anyone but themselves.

I remain the only female faculty member in the department who has ever had a kid on the tenure track. I remember mentioning this fact in the presence of a woman assistant professor; there were other people around. She rushed to point out that a male colleague of ours (who has a stay-at-home wife), also had a kid on the tenure track. While new fathers do suffer some sleep deprivation in the baby's first year, it is *not* the same as for a new mother, especially one who breastfeeds. This male colleague had no problem working 12-hour days starting the week his kid was born (perhaps hiding from the baby?). I was a complete zombie for many months after birth, definitely not 100 percent, physically or mentally. What truly pissed me off was that the first reaction of my (childfree) female colleague was to trivialize my experience. I didn't want to continue the conversation and regurgitate the tired (but true) spiel of how women have it harder than men when the child is born — whoever does not see that does not *want* to see it. But I remember this situation as one of many in which I have found the female camaraderie to be completely nonexistent.

My collaborators are overwhelmingly male (95 percent of them). A number of them are close to my age, having two or three kids. They all have stay-at-home wives; my husband works full time. Over the years, the subject of work–life balance has come up a few times with my male collaborators, and after a few sentences I see they no longer want to talk about it. They consider my job and my obligations to be exactly like those they have and when there emerges a hint that they may not be, they rush to change the subject.

I wish that I could tell my male colleagues that, in addition to all the work at the actual job that I have to do, which is the same as theirs, I am still mommy and do all the nonnegotiable mommy duties that their wives do and a significant load of chores. I don't know how much my male colleagues with stay-at-home wives do at home, but I can't imagine they do more than my husband, who also works full time.

That's what I would like to tell my male colleagues if they cared to hear; they likely know all this, but simply don't care. Many times I have had to cancel a meeting when a kid is sick; I do not recall any of my male colleagues with kids having ever done that. I have yet to see any of them, whose kids are of similar ages to mine, cut down on the number of trips or meetings because of their kids; they don't have to, because there is always their wife to pick up the slack. But that doesn't matter — since I have the same job as them, if I cannot cut it, it's my weakness; I should make it work and not whine about hardship or ask for special consideration. Right?

While it's nice to read all these calls for work–life balance on the Internet, when it comes to real life, most of us only care about ourselves. If balance for all means sometimes shouldering a bit more because someone else temporarily cannot, and especially if they cannot because of personal choices that we ourselves would not make, then the concept of balance becomes unacceptable;

instead, rigid rules must be followed and complete sacrifice at the altar of work is expected. It is oh so very, very unfair that all the righteous workers who don't harbor uterine squatters end up picking up the slack after our lazy postpartum asses.

On Working Long Hours

Years ago, I had a conversation with my then soon-to-graduate PhD student. He had interviewed for a postdoc with a good group and secured the position. His future boss wanted him to start as soon as possible. The student and I agreed long ago on what he needed to do before graduation: he needed to finish a major part of his project, write and submit a paper from his project that would include this major technical part, write up quality documentation for his code, and obviously write his dissertation (the dissertation should not have taken very long, once all the relevant papers were written up). The goal was to have him tentatively finish everything by the end of summer.

Now, the student had been stuck on a technical issue for a while now, and was not making much progress on either calculations or paper writing. I told him to go work on code documentation or those parts of his dissertation that didn't require this particular set of data. Since he needed to graduate sooner rather than later, this would have been a good use of his time and should have also helped with the technical challenge by freeing his mind and letting it gnaw on the problem in the background. However, the student basically refused, saying that he could do all that later (cobbling code documentation at the last minute is not the way to produce a quality document) and that he couldn't work like me (?!), that he preferred to work on one thing at a time, immersing himself completely, until completely done.

Couldn't work like me? Because I obviously *love* being interrupted all the time by the various things I have to do, and I could not *possibly* prefer to work on one thing at a time, immersing myself completely, until completely done.

Working on one thing at a time, for as long as you need to or feel like it, *is a luxury*. It means there is no one else who depends on you; no one to pick up from school, make dinner for, or wipe the butts of; no one who is on your team at work and needs your part of the project to get their own assignments done. I cannot tell you how many times it happened that I am in the middle of something exciting at work, and all of a sudden it's 5 o'clock, time to pick up the kids and go home to make dinner. My preference to stay immersed in my work is completely irrelevant.

There is something intoxicating about working long hours on something challenging. I have been known to really enjoy pulling all-nighters; the adrenaline makes me feel alive. But, after an extended period of such work, I invariably crash. I can no longer routinely put in long hours or pull all-nighters followed by comatose periods, because it's not fair to my husband, who then has to take care of the kids, and it is not fair to my kids. Recently, I had a really busy period because of the conference I was organizing. This period included several weeks of working very long hours, a week where I did not see my kids at all even though I was in town, followed by a week to recuperate. I don't have the right to put this much strain on my family on a regular basis.

Lastly, there is sleep. I have had students who work regular hours and those who work and sleep erratic hours, in bursts. The most productive people have been those with regular work-days — come in the morning, work hard, go home in the evening and relax. People with erratic sleep and work habits ended up not being as productive overall as they could have been, because they'd get sick more often than average and were consistently pushing themselves beyond optimal efficiency.

In my own personal and professional lives, there are many balls to juggle. I need to be in fighting shape for my family, for my students and coworkers, which means I need to be healthy and rested, both of which require enough sleep. Not that I am getting as much sleep as I need as regularly as possible, but I'm getting better at it. Sleeping enough makes all the difference to my energy levels and my mood.

Adapting your modus operandi to accommodate all the different people who depend on you for different things is not a personality trait; I particularly resent it when people imply it's somehow a feminine one. It is about recognizing that your life is no longer all about you and what you want, about accepting your responsibilities. It's called being a grown-up.

Manicure That

I caught a glimpse of #ManicureMondays, a Twitter hashtag put forth by a teenage-girl magazine and temporarily hijacked by female scientists. I am not on Twitter and I don't care enough to follow the whole thing in any considerable detail, so I am going by what I saw on one blog and a couple of immediate links. The women scientists showed off their hands doing science, but many of the nails were short and unmanicured. Now there is a concern that the manicured ones are not welcome in science.

Seriously? Science is awesome. If your interest in science is so feeble that a side eye over nail fashion would discourage it, perhaps you shouldn't do it. I don't care if this makes me sound like a tool of the patriarchy; nails are simply too stupid a reason to worry about when it comes to the lack of women in STEM. I *sooooo* truly deeply don't give a damn what anyone's hands look like that it's not even funny. (I probably care more what someone's feet look like, especially if they are going to inflict them upon me in flip-flops.)

I used to have long nails and wear bulky hand jewelry throughout my youth. Then at some point I had baby #1, and a few months into motherhood the nails and most of my bulky rings went away and I haven't really looked back since. Short nails make doing most things with your hands easier; that's simply the truth. If you care about how your nails look so you are willing to put up with minor or not-so-minor inconveniences, more power to you. I refuse to believe that a manicure is a political statement.

The same thing about makeup. Most of my colleagues wear none, and I don't just mean the men. I wear some makeup most days. I also wear pants all the time. And sometimes I wear some jewelry. These are not political or feminist statements; they are barely fashion statements. Mostly, they are statements on how much time I had in the morning, whether my kids slept well, whether someone dropped my eye shadow on the bathroom tile and shattered it five minutes before it was time to leave.

Sometimes I care about looking pretty or put together, sometimes I just don't.

I cannot believe that we think our young girls, especially those serious about academics, would think that liking nail polish or makeup will make them unqualified. It seems we have a really low opinion of them. Sure, someone might discriminate against them at some point, or at a lot of points, but we should not be force-feeding them these prognoses of doom and gloom when they are in middle school and believe they can conquer the world. If you want a career in a male-dominated field, you cannot be a shrinking violet anyway. Someone thinking that your nails look stupid or that you are not serious because you have a manicure better receive lots or ridicule and a new-orifice tearing from you in the technical arena so he (or she) never makes the same mistaken assumption again.

I am just pissed that we feel the need to be concerned that future women scientists will be turned away because we, as practicing women scientists, appear not to be accepting of manicures. Our future women scientists are neither that shallow nor that stupid. It's goddamn nail polish, for crying out loud.

Oversharing

Academic women who are about to have kids often worry how much this temporary slow-down for family will hurt their careers. I find that everyone seems to understand being out for a few months to take care of a newborn. However, people are considerably more judgmental of all the absences that stem from doctor's appointments, sick-kid early pickups from daycare, and other disasters that accompany raising small children.

Avoid discussing what your absences mean. I learned this from a senior female colleague who is such a master of aloofness and pinnacle of respectability that everyone thinks she's a deity. Are you covering your teaching and nonnegotiable service? Yes? Excellent! How you organize your time beyond that is essentially nobody's business. You could be going to a string of conferences or review panels, right? You are simply not available — that's what most people need to know.

That colleague I mentioned simply says, "This week does not work for me." No explanation. If you want to meet with her, you have to propose another date and time. Whether she is doing aerobics all week, or is at a conference, or her kid is sick — no one knows.

Anecdotally, when men are away, people assume they are away on business. When women are away, people assume it's because of family. Don't give them ammunition to further stereotype you.

And don't worry about putting research on the back burner temporarily. The work–family balance is never a balance; it's more like a seesaw. When a kid is sick, of course work has lower priority. Luckily, kids really seem not to get sick very often past a year or two in a childcare setting.

Benevolently Sexist

One of these days, I will have to have a talk with a colleague who has an administrative role. His heart is in the right place and he is one of the men who really support women and their advancement in the physical sciences, as evidenced by him propelling his female colleagues and students. However, I think he might have inadvertently gotten lost in the thick forest of benevolent sexism.

For probably several years now, he has been spearheading this notion, backed by research but not in the literal form he seems to espouse, that we need to pitch our field as the haven for those people who want to help others and that we need to do it specifically so that we would attract more women students.

One the one hand, I understand what his real motivation is. Being head of a department, his role is to bring in students, because high enrollments mean high importance to the college and the university. In that sense, one cannot begrudge him for wanting to cast a wider net by any means necessary.

On the other hand, there are several things that are sexist about this attitude. First, it assumes that, deep down, all women want to be caretakers, and that one has to appeal to a smart woman's inner nurse in order to bring her — nay, trick her! — into the physical sciences. It also assumes that while men are naturally geeks, women could not possibly be real geeks or like the physical sciences for the same reasons as men, or for any reasons unrelated to their inner warmth and fuzziness.

I don't know what one has to do to get this through people's skulls: there are women geeks. Honestly, they exist. *Raises hand to be counted.* There are women who like and are very good at math, physics, chemistry, computer science; who play video games; who like science fiction and fantasy.

Women geeks and men geeks do not necessarily look and act like the stereotypes. One can be into math, physics, chemistry, or computers, and at the same time also look perfectly presentable and be perfectly socially adjusted. One can be into math, physics, chemistry, or computers, and also have long hair, boobs, and wear lipstick.

Not all women are motivated by helping those around them. In my choice of career, helping people didn't figure in one iota. I like what I like because it's intellectually challenging and fun. If anyone had come to pitch math or physics as a means of helping people when I was young, I would have probably run away from them as fast as I could. (Women can also be misanthropes, just like men.)

Not all men are motivated by the same things, either. Shocking, I know. There are plenty of men who want to help others. It boggles my mind that we as a society seem OK with stereotyping men as robot-loving geeks. I bet there are many boys who went into premed majors and whom we could have perhaps swayed into the physical sciences with the "physical sciences — because we are all about helping people!" pitch, the same one that supposedly mesmerizes the ever-elusive girls into majoring in STEM.

There are a variety of reasons why people choose to do what they do. We should try to understand the reasons and expand the appeal of our field as best we can to try to attract more students. But please let's do that in a way that does not enforce gender stereotypes.

Let's not insist women don't come unless you appeal to their inner nurturer. Some girls simply like computers and robots, period. Pitching soft at women and hard at men only further perpetuates the idea that women are not real physical scientists. It also pushes away the men who may care about their fellow humans and would be motivated by the human-centered aspect of the physical sciences. And it also makes many men resentful, because they perceive that the field is being softened and moving away from its essence because of those darn women.

The physical-science fields are what they are. Let's be honest as well as open-minded when we report about the opportunities the fields offer (good job prospects, anyone?). But let's also be honest about the skills and interests that are required to succeed, and let us enhance the appeal without benevolently perpetuating the stereotype that women could not possibly be capable of swallowing the bitter science pill without the sugarcoat of nurture.

About the Author

Sydney Phlox is a professor at a large public research university in the US, working in one of the science, technology, engineering, and math (STEM) fields. She loves quantum mechanics, science fiction, and bad puns. She and her husband raise a prime number of unruly children and drive in the snow like champs. Phlox blogs and doodles at xykademiqz.wordpress.com.

About the Publisher

Annorlunda Books is a small press that publishes books to inform, entertain, and make you think. We publish short books (novella length or shorter) and collections of short writing, fiction and non-fiction.

Find more information about us and our books online: annorlundaenterprises.com/books, on Twitter: @AnnorlundaInc, or on Facebook: facebook.com/annorlundabooks.

To stay up to date on all of our releases, subscribe to our mailing list at annorlundaenterprises.com/mailing-list.

Other Titles from Annorlunda Books

Original Short eBooks

Don't Call It Bollywood, by Margaret E. Redlich, is an introduction to the world of Hindi film, with stories from the author's own path to dedicated fandom interspersed with analysis of the history and artistic context of these films.

Okay, So Look, by Micah Edwards, is a humorous, yet accurate and thought-provoking, retelling of The Book of Genesis.

Navigating the Path to Industry, by M.R. Nelson, is a hiring manager's advice on how to run a successful non-academic job search.

Unspotted, by Justin Fox, is the story of the Cape Mountain Leopard, the scientist dedicated to saving these rare and elusive big cats, and the author's own journey to try to see one.

Taster Flights

Missed Chances is a Taster Flight collection of classic stories about love. In each of its five stories, there is a hint of "the one that got away."

Love and Other Happy Endings is another Taster Flight of classic stories, all of which end on a high note.

Made in the USA
Middletown, DE
25 July 2018